Section Four — Geometry and Measures

Section Five — Pythagoras and Trigonometry

Section Six — Statistics and Probability

Published by CGP

Editors:
Shaun Harrogate, Caley Simpson and Michael Weynberg.

Contributor:
Alastair Duncombe

With thanks to Sammy El-Bahrawy for the proofreading.

ISBN: 978 1 78908 239 5

Clipart from Corel®
Printed by Elanders Ltd, Newcastle upon Tyne

Based on the classic CGP style created by Richard Parsons.

It's another great book from CGP...

Getting a top grade in Edexcel International GCSE Maths is no picnic.
There are plenty of topics in the exams that could trip you up on the day.

That's why we've made this brilliant book. It's packed with exam-style
questions covering the most difficult parts of the course — if you can
answer this lot, you won't get any nasty shocks in the exam.

We've also included fully-worked answers, so if you drop any marks,
it's easy to find out exactly where you went wrong.

CGP — still the best! ☺

Our sole aim here at CGP is to produce the highest quality books —
carefully written, immaculately presented and dangerously close to being funny.

Then we work our socks off to get them out to you
— at the cheapest possible prices.

Contents

Use the tick boxes to check off the topics you've completed.

Exam Tips

Exam Stuff

1) For your Edexcel International GCSE Mathematics course you will have <u>two</u> exams — both are calculator exams.

2) Each exam is 2 hours long and is worth <u>100 marks</u>.

3) Timings in the exam are really important, so here's a quick guide...

- As each paper is worth <u>100 marks</u> and you've got <u>120 minutes</u> to complete the paper, you should spend about a <u>minute per mark</u> working on each question (i.e. 2 marks = 2 mins).

- The <u>hardest questions</u> will come towards the end of each exam and are often worth the <u>most marks</u>, so give yourself plenty of time to tackle them.

- Use any spare time at the end of the exam to <u>check</u> back through your answers and make sure you haven't made any silly mistakes. <u>Not</u> to just stare at that hottie in front.

Here are a Few Handy Hints

1) **Don't let <u>easy marks</u> slip through your fingers.**
   To give yourself the best chance of getting the highest grades you'll need to cut out as many <u>silly mistakes</u> as possible. <u>Read the question</u> properly, give your answer to the right <u>degree of accuracy</u>, give the <u>correct units</u> where needed and always <u>check your answer</u> is sensible.

2) **Show <u>each step</u> in your <u>working</u>.**
   You're less likely to make a mistake if you write things out clearly and in stages. Even if your final answer's wrong, you might pick up a few method marks if you've shown all your working.

3) **Look at the number of <u>marks</u> a question is worth.**
   If a question's worth 2 or more marks its probably going to require you to do a few steps. Make sure you write down what you're doing at each stage.

4) **Give <u>exact</u> answers when the question asks you to.**
   When you're asked for an <u>exact answer</u> you'll probably need to leave your answer as a surd, in terms of π or as a fraction. <u>Don't round</u> at any stage in your calculation.

   These handy hints might help you pick up a couple of extra marks — but they're no use if you haven't learnt the stuff in the first place. So make sure you revise well and do as many practice questions as you can.

5) **Learn the <u>formulas</u>.**
   Some of the formulas you'll need in your exams <u>won't</u> be given to you, so <u>learn them</u>.

Using Your Calculator

1) Before your exam, clear the memory of your calculator and check that it's in <u>degrees mode</u>. This is important for any <u>trigonometry</u> questions.

2) If you're working out a <u>big calculation</u> on your calculator, it's best to do it in <u>stages</u> and use the <u>memory</u> to store the answers to the different parts. If you try and do it all in one go, it's easy to mess it up.

3) If you're going to be a renegade and do a question all in one go on your calculator, use <u>brackets</u> so the calculator knows which bits to do first.

REMEMBER: <u>The 2nd Handy Hint</u> still applies, even if you're using a calculator — you should still write down <u>all</u> the steps you are doing so the examiner can see the method you're using.

Fractions and Recurring Decimals

1   Look at this fraction sum: $\dfrac{a}{11} + \dfrac{b}{6} = 0.\dot{7}\dot{5}$.

   a)   Use algebra to convert $0.\dot{7}\dot{5}$ to a fraction in its simplest form.

....
[2]

   b)   Work out the values of *a* and *b*, given that they are positive integers.

a = ..., *b* = ...
[3]
[Total 5 marks]

2   Some square wall tiles have a side length of $2.\dot{2}$ cm.
Heather wants to cover an area of 1600 cm² with these tiles.

   a)   Convert the side length of a wall tile into a fraction algebraically.

.... cm
[2]

   b)   Given that she can cover the area exactly with whole tiles,
work out the number of tiles she will need to use.

....
[2]
[Total 4 marks]

3   By convert the recurring decimal to a fraction algebraically, solve the
equation below. Give your answer as a fraction in its simplest form.

$$\frac{7x - 3}{6} = 0.1\dot{4}\dot{2}$$

x = ...
[Total 4 marks]

Score: ☐

13

Percentages

1 In the first quarter of the year a company's sales were £12 million. In each of the next three quarters, sales were 10% higher than the previous quarter. 28% of the company's sales are profit. At the end of the year 30% of the company profits are given to the employees as a bonus.

How much was given to the employees as a bonus?
Give your answer to 2 significant figures.

There are 4 quarters in a year.

£ ....
[Total 4 marks]

2 Simone took 3 maths exams. She scored 85% on exam A, which was out of 120 marks and 50% on exam B, which was out of 80 marks. On exam C she scored 95%.

She scored 75% of the total marks across the 3 exams. How many marks was exam C out of?

.... marks
[Total 4 marks]

3 Two cubes, *A* and *B*, have the same weight. Both are resting on horizontal ground. The side length of cube *B* is 20% longer than the side length of cube *A*.

Give the pressure that cube *A* exerts as a percentage of the pressure that cube *B* exerts.

Pressure = force ÷ area

.... %
[Total 4 marks]

4 An investment company guarantees 10% interest on a customer's investment per annum. At the end of each year the company takes any money above the 10% interest as a payment and reinvests the rest of the customer's money.

One customer's 3-year investment of £100 000 makes 12% interest per annum.
How much does the company make over the 3 years from this customer's investment?

£ ....

[Total 5 marks]

5 The pie charts show the types of houses in two villages.

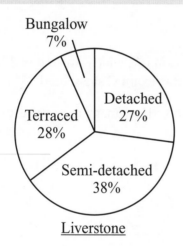

Liverstone

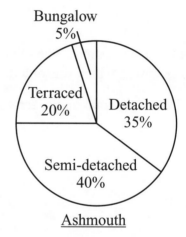

Ashmouth

There are 480 more terraced houses in Ashmouth than in Liverstone.
Ashmouth has 70% more houses in total than Liverstone.

Calculate how many more semi-detached houses there are in Ashmouth than in Liverstone.

Start by writing the number of houses in Ashmouth in terms of the number of houses in Liverstone (L).

....

[Total 5 marks]

Score:

22

Ratios

1   A rowing boat travelled 18 km in 2 hours 15 minutes.
A canoe travelled 8000 m in 30 minutes.

What is the approximate ratio of the speed of the rowing boat to the speed of the canoe?
Give your answer in its simplest form.

....

[Total 4 marks]

2   Abbey draws two triangles, *A* and *B*.
The height of triangle *B* is 1 cm more than the height of triangle *A*.
The bases of triangle *A* and triangle *B* are in the ratio $1:3$.
The areas of triangle *A* and triangle *B* are in the ratio $2:9$. Triangle *B* has an area of 45 cm².

What is the ratio of the vertical height of triangle *A* to the vertical height of triangle *B*?

....

[Total 5 marks]

3   Jenna and Harvey both play a computer game.
The percentages of the game Jenna and Harvey have completed are in the ratio $3:4$.
If they were both to complete another 7% of the game, the ratio would become $7:9$.

What percentage of the game has Jenna completed?

.... %

[Total 4 marks]

4 At a school there are x Year 8 pupils and y Year 9 pupils.
If 10 pupils from each year group left the school, the ratio of pupils in Year 8 to Year 9 would be $2:5$. If 8 pupils were added to each year group, the ratio would be $1:2$.

Express x as a percentage of y.

.... %

[Total 5 marks]

5 A bag contains sweets that are either red, yellow or green.
The bag contains equal numbers of red and green sweets.

Luke eats 5 red, 15 yellow and 25 green sweets from the bag.
The ratio of red to yellow sweets remaining in the bag is $2:3$
The ratio of yellow to green sweets remaining in the bag is $3:1$

What fraction of the sweets originally in the bag were yellow?
Give your answer in its simplest form.

....

[Total 6 marks]

Score:

24

Bounds

1 Look at the formula below.

$$4z^3 = \frac{\left(x^{\frac{1}{2}}y^{-3}z\right)^2}{y^{-5}}$$

a) Rearrange the formula to make z the subject.

....
[3]

b) If $x = 6.8$ and $y = 1.2$, both rounded to one decimal place, work out the upper bound for z.
    Give your answer to 3 significant figures.

....
[3]

[Total 6 marks]

2 Shannon is performing in a gymnastics competition. Her overall score is calculated
   by adding together the scores for each piece of equipment. Her scores for each
   piece of equipment, correct to 4 significant figures, are shown below.

   Floor: 16.42   Beam: 13.15   Bars: 14.88   Vault: x

Shannon is in the lead by exactly 0.05 points. The person in 2nd place has a score of
60.15 correct to 4 significant figures. What is the lowest possible value of x?

....
[Total 3 marks]

3 *A* and *B* are similar shapes.

$a = 6.2$ cm correct to the nearest 0.1 cm
$b = 3.5$ cm correct to the nearest 0.1 cm
$c = 11.8$ cm correct to the nearest 0.1 cm

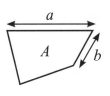

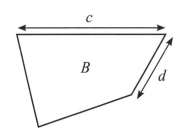

Calculate the minimum possible value for the length d.

Scale factor = new length ÷ old length

.... cm
[Total 4 marks]

Section One — Numbers

4 The circle opposite represents a pizza.
The shaded sector shows a slice of pizza with area S cm².

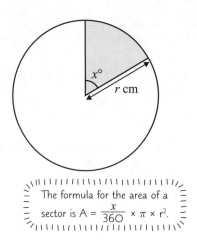

$S = 179.2$ correct to 1 decimal place.
$x = 60$ correct to the nearest whole number.
The length r cm is the radius of the pizza.

Find the lower and upper bounds for the radius of the pizza.
Give your answers to 2 decimal places.

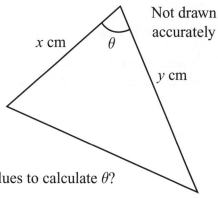

The formula for the area of a sector is $A = \frac{x}{360} \times \pi \times r^2$.

Lower bound .... cm

Upper bound .... cm

[Total 5 marks]

5 The diagram shows a triangle with area A cm².

$A = 2900$ to 2 significant figures.
$x = 97.0$ to 3 significant figures.
$y = 78.9$ to 3 significant figures.

Not drawn accurately

x cm θ

y cm

θ is an acute angle.
The value of θ can be found using this formula: $\sin \theta = \frac{2A}{xy}$

What is the maximum possible error if you use the rounded values to calculate θ?
Give your answer to 3 significant figures.

Work out the lower and upper bounds for θ and compare them to the calculation using the rounded values.

°

....

[Total 7 marks]

Exam practice tip

Take extra care when you have rounded values on the top and bottom of a fraction (like in question 5).
The maximum value of the fraction occurs when values in the numerator equal their upper bounds and
values in the denominator equal their lower bounds. For the minimum value it's the other way round.

Score

25

Standard Form

1 A shipping container has a weight of 4.2×10^4 N to 2 significant figures.
The area of the base of the shipping container is 30 m² to 1 significant figure.

The deck of a cargo ship has a pressure restriction of 1600 N/m². Is it safe for the shipping container to be transported on the cargo ship? Show working to support your answer.

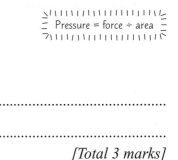
Pressure = force ÷ area

....

....

[Total 3 marks]

2 The Heron Sea has a volume of 1.4×10^{14} litres, of which 12% is salt.
The Cobalt Sea has a volume of 8.5×10^{12} litres, of which 8% is salt.

What is the percentage decrease in the volume of salt from the Heron Sea to the Cobalt Sea? Give your answer to 2 decimal places.

.... %

[Total 3 marks]

3 $a = 2^{10} \times 5^9$, $b = 9\,000\,000$, $c = 2.4 \times 10^9$
Work out the lowest common multiple of a, b and c.

Give your answer in standard form.

....

[Total 4 marks]

Score: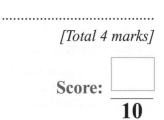

10

Sets and Venn Diagrams

1   In the Venn diagram on the right,
   F = people who play football.
   R = people who play rugby.

   15 people play football. 13 people play rugby.
   Find the number of people who play both.

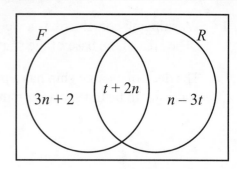

....
[Total 5 marks]

2   The Venn diagram below shows the sets A, B, C and the universal set ξ.

   Each number on the diagram represents the **number** of elements.

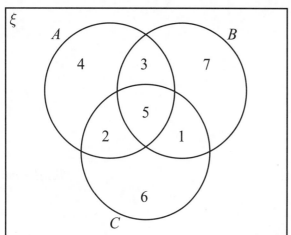

a)   Find n$(A \cup B)$.

....
[1]

b)   What fraction of the elements in
   set C are also in set $A' \cup B$?

....
[2]

c)   Using set notation, give the set that:

   (i) only contains one element.

....
[1]

   (ii) is a subset of $A \cap C$.

....
[1]

[Total 5 marks]

Exam practice tip

Read Venn diagram questions carefully to avoid making mistakes. A common error is to confuse the number
of elements in a set with the number of elements <u>only</u> in that set. For example, in question 1, the number of
people in set F is $(3n + 2) + (t + 2n)$, not $3n + 2$ (this is the number of people that are <u>only in set F</u>).

Score

10

Section One — Numbers

Powers and Surds

1   Expand and simplify $(\sqrt{5} - 6)^3$. Give your answer in the form $a + b\sqrt{5}$.

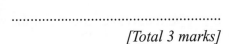

[Total 3 marks]

2   Simplify fully $a^7 \times \left(25a^6 b^{10} c^5\right)^{\frac{1}{2}}$.

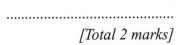

[Total 2 marks]

3   Write $\sqrt{343} + \dfrac{21}{\sqrt{7}} - 4\sqrt{252}$ in the form $a\sqrt{b}$, where a and b are integers.

Show each stage of your working.

[Total 4 marks]

4   Given that $\left(\dfrac{729}{8x}\right)^{\frac{1}{3}} = \dfrac{9}{4}$, find the value of x.

$x =$ ....
[Total 2 marks]

5   Find the exact volume of the cuboid on the right.

Give your answer in the form $a + b\sqrt{5}$, where a and b are integers.
Show each stage of your working.

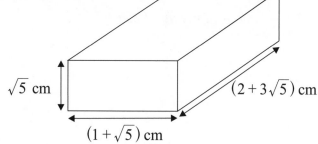

Not drawn accurately

$\sqrt{5}$ cm

$(2 + 3\sqrt{5})$ cm

$(1 + \sqrt{5})$ cm

.... cm^3
[Total 4 marks]

6 $a = 3b^3 + 2b^6$, where $b = \left(4c + 3\right)^{\frac{1}{3}}$

Express a in terms of c, simplifying your answer as much as possible.

....
[Total 3 marks]

Section Two — Algebra

7 Simplify $\dfrac{2\sqrt{3}}{3+\sqrt{3}} + \dfrac{2+\sqrt{3}}{2-\sqrt{3}}$.

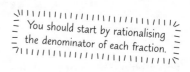
You should start by rationalising the denominator of each fraction.

Show each stage of your working.

....

[Total 5 marks]

8 Find the values of x and y, given that $\left(\dfrac{64}{49}\right)^{-\frac{x}{y}} = \dfrac{343}{512}$.

$x = $ .... , $y = $ ....

[Total 3 marks]

9 Simplify $\dfrac{(1+2\sqrt{2})^2}{\sqrt{2}-1}$.

Show each stage of your working.

....

[Total 4 marks]

Exam Practice Tip

No doubt about it — surds are tricksy little devils. Always remember to simplify your answers as much as possible — if you have a big number in a surd, see if it'll divide by a square number to simplify it some more. The smaller the surd, the easier it is to deal with — especially if you're trying to combine a few different surds.

Score

30

Section Two — Algebra

Quadratic Equations

1 The surface area of a sphere is $36\pi x^2 + 48\pi x + 16\pi$ cm^2,
where x is positive. Find the radius of the sphere in terms of x.

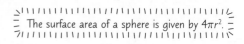
The surface area of a sphere is given by $4\pi r^2$.

.... cm

[Total 3 marks]

2 Look at the quadratic equation $2x^2 - 3x - 35 = 0$.

a) Fully factorise the expression $2x^2 - 3x - 35$.

....

[2]

b) Use your answer to part a) to solve the equation $2(2x-1)^2 - 3(2x-1) - 35 = 0$.

$x = $ .... or $x = $ ....

[3]

[Total 5 marks]

3 Solve the equation $\dfrac{x}{2x+1} - \dfrac{x+3}{x-1} = 2$.

$x = $ .... or $x = $ ....

[Total 4 marks]

Section Two — Algebra

4 Look at the quadratic equation $3x^2 - 14x - 24 = 0$.

a) Fully factorise the expression $3x^2 - 14x - 24$.

....

[2]

b) Use your answer to part a) to solve the equation $3x^2 - 14x - 24 = (3x + 4)^2$.

Remember — you're looking for two solutions here.

$x =$ .... or $x =$ ....

[4]

[Total 6 marks]

5 The surface area of a cylinder with height 1 m is 31π m². Find r, the exact radius of the cylinder in its simplest form.

The surface area of a cylinder is given by $2\pi rh + 2\pi r^2$.

$r =$ .... m

[Total 4 marks]

6 Calculate the positive value of $\dfrac{1}{1 - 3x}$ if $\dfrac{1}{x} + \dfrac{6}{x + 2} = 5$.

$x =$ ....

[Total 5 marks]

Score:

27

Section Two — Algebra

Completing the Square

1 Write the expression $x^2 + 7x + 11$ in the form $(x + a)^2 + b$.

....

[Total 3 marks]

2 $3x^2 + sx + 29$ can be written in the form $r(x + 4)^2 + t$, where r, s and t are integers.

By finding the values of r, s and t, work out the coordinates
of the turning point of the curve $y = 3x^2 + sx + 29$.

....

[Total 4 marks]

3 Look at the quadratic equation $5x^2 + 20x + 12 = 0$.

a) Write the expression $5x^2 + 20x + 12$ in the form $u(x + v)^2 + w$.

....

[4]

b) Hence find the solutions of $5x^2 + 20x + 12 = 0$. Give your answers to 3 significant figures.

$x = $ .... or $x = $ ....

[2]

[Total 6 marks]

Exam Practice Tip

Completing the square can be really nasty — but remember, you can always check your answer by expanding
your completed square form and checking that you end up with the original equation. It's easy to make
mistakes when there are a load of awkward fractions flying around, so take your time and don't rush or panic.

Score

13

Algebraic Fractions

1   Simplify fully $\dfrac{2v^2 - 18}{v^2 + 3v} \times \dfrac{v^2 - v}{v^2 + 8v - 9}$.

....

[Total 5 marks]

2   Let $a = 5x^2 - 80y^2$ and $b = 40y - 10x$. Find an expression for $\dfrac{1}{a} \div \dfrac{1}{b}$.

Give your answer in its simplest form.

....

[Total 4 marks]

3   Write $\dfrac{3}{x} + \dfrac{2x}{x + 4}$ as a single fraction.

....

[Total 3 marks]

4   Simplify fully $\dfrac{x + 7}{x^2} \times \dfrac{x^2 + 2x}{x^2 - 49} \times \dfrac{6x - 42}{3x + 6}$.

....

[Total 5 marks]

5 Write $\frac{1}{x^2} + \frac{x+3}{x-2} - \frac{4}{x}$ as a single fraction.

....

[Total 4 marks]

6 Simplify fully $\frac{x^2-5}{2x^2-7x-4} \times \frac{2x+1}{x-\sqrt{5}}$.

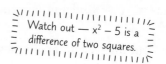

Watch out — $x^2 - 5$ is a difference of two squares.

....

[Total 3 marks]

7 Show that $\frac{14x-35}{2x^2+x-15} \div \frac{4xy-12y}{2x^2y-18y} = k$, where k is a number to be found.

[Total 6 marks]

Score:

30

Quadratic Inequalities

1   Solve the inequality $x^2 + x - 56 < 0$.

....

[Total 3 marks]

2   Look at the grid on the right.

On the grid, shade the region(s) that satisfies the inequalities below:
$$y \leq 3$$
$$y + x \leq 5$$
$$4x - x^2 \leq 0$$

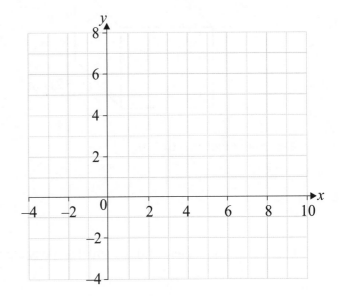

[Total 4 marks]

3   The sum of the areas of the circles below is greater than 160π cm^2.

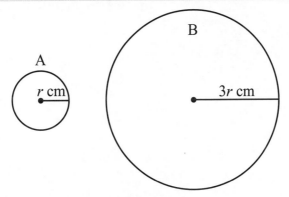

Given that r is an integer, find the smallest possible radius of each circle.

radius of circle A = ... cm, radius of circle B = ... cm

[Total 3 marks]

4   Solve the inequality $3x^2 - x - 90 \geq 5x + 15$.

....

[Total 4 marks]

5   Look at the two cuboids below. The volume of cuboid B is greater than the volume of cuboid A.

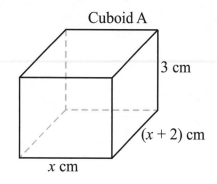
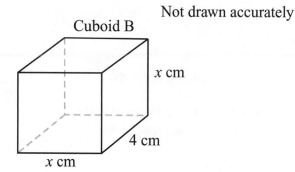

Cuboid A

Cuboid B

Not drawn accurately

3 cm

x cm

$(x + 2)$ cm

4 cm

x cm

x cm

a)   Show that $x^2 - 6x > 0$.

[3]

b)   If x is an integer, find the smallest possible volume of cuboid B.

.... cm³

[4]

[Total 7 marks]

6   Solve the inequality $x^2 \leq \dfrac{23x - 45}{2}$.

....

[Total 4 marks]

Exam Practice Tip

It's always a good idea to very quickly sketch the quadratic graph to work out which bit of it you want (either above or below the x-axis, depending on the inequality sign). This will tell you whether you want a solution within an enclosed region (e.g. $-1 < x < 1$) or a solution in two separate bits (e.g. $x < -1$ and $x > 1$).

Score

25

Simultaneous Equations

1   Solve the following pair of simultaneous equations.

$$x^2 + 4y^2 = 37$$
$$2x - y = x + 4$$

$x =$ .... , $y =$ ....

and $x =$ .... , $y =$ ....

[Total 5 marks]

2   The shape below is made up of two rectangles with dimensions as shown. The total area of the shape is 83 cm², and the total base length is 9 cm.

Find the values of x and y, given that they are both integers.

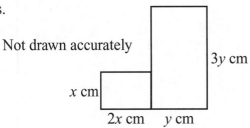

Not drawn accurately

x cm

$3y$ cm

$2x$ cm y cm

$x =$ .... , $y =$ ....

[Total 5 marks]

3   The line $7x - y = 25$ intersects the circle $x^2 + y^2 = 25$ at two points, A and B. Find the exact length of the line AB. Give your answer in its simplest form.

....

[Total 6 marks]

Section Two — Algebra

4 The cuboid below has a weight of 120 N. When the cuboid rests on face *A*, the pressure exerted is 10 N/m². When the cuboid rests on face *B*, the pressure exerted is 7.5 N/m².

Find the volume of the cuboid.

Not drawn accurately

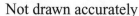

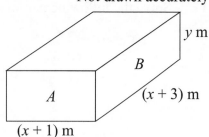

Use the formula pressure = force ÷ area to form two simultaneous equations.

y m

B

$(x + 3)$ m

A

$(x + 1)$ m

.... m³

[Total 6 marks]

5 The line $y = 2x - 5$ intersects the curve $y = -x^2 + 15x - 41$ at the points *A* and *B*, as shown.

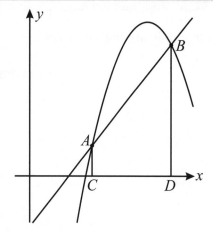

C and *D* are points on the *x*-axis. The lines *CA* and *DB* are parallel to the *y*-axis.
Calculate the area of the quadrilateral *ABDC*.

.... units²

[Total 6 marks]

Exam Practice Tip

Remember, you can always check your x- and y-values by putting them back into the original equations and checking they produce the numbers given in the question. If they don't, you've gone wrong somewhere. Check your factorising — it's easy to make a mistake (especially with tricky numbers).

Score

28

Sequences

1   A sequence has *n*th term $5n - 3$.

What is the value of the first term in the sequence that is greater than the sum of the first 77 terms?

....
[Total 4 marks]

2   The number of entries into a weekly competition follows an arithmetic sequence.
On week 3 there were 18 entries. Over the first 9 weeks there were a total of 288 entries.

How many entries will there be in the 30th week?

....
[Total 5 marks]

3   The first, second and third terms of an arithmetic sequence
are $6x + 1$, $8x - 29$ and $5x + 6$, where *x* is an integer.

Find the 20th term in the sequence.

> In an arithmetic sequence, the difference between each consecutive pair of terms is the same.

....
[Total 6 marks]

Score:

15

Section Two — Algebra

Proof

1   Prove that $(2n + 1)^3 - 1 \equiv 2n(4n^2 + 6n + 3)$.

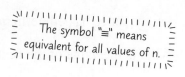

The symbol "$\equiv$" means equivalent for all values of n.

[Total 3 marks]

2   Prove algebraically that for any 2 consecutive integers the difference between their squares is equal to their sum.

[Total 3 marks]

3   If a and b are both odd, prove that $(a + b)^{40}$ is even.

[Total 2 marks]

4   Prove that the sum of any three consecutive cube numbers is a multiple of 3.

[Total 4 marks]

5   Max thinks of a whole number that is one more than a multiple of 5.
Samira thinks of the number that is four less than Max's number.

Prove that the difference in the squares of their values is a multiple of 8.

[Total 5 marks]

6   Show that $3^8 - 7^4$ is a multiple of 13.

[Total 3 marks]

7   Show that the sum of 15^{12} and 12^{16} is a multiple of 9.

Start by writing 15^{12} and 12^{16} as products of their prime factors.

[Total 3 marks]

Score:

23

Section Two — Algebra

Direct and Inverse Proportion

1 When a motorbike is travelling at 70 km/h, the amount of fuel used, f litres, is directly proportional to the distance travelled, d km. When $d = 84$, $f = 3$.

a) Write an equation connecting f and d.

....
[3]

b) How much fuel will the motorbike use travelling at 70 km/h for 5.4 hours?

.... litres
[2]

[Total 5 marks]

2 The weight, w g, of a sphere is directly proportional to the cube of its radius, r cm.

a) When the radius is 6 cm, the sphere weighs 1080 g.
What is the radius of a sphere weighing 8.64 kg?

.... cm
[4]

b) Sketch the graph of w against r on the axes on the right.

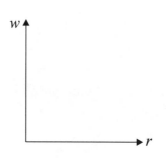

[1]
[Total 5 marks]

3 p is directly proportional to q and q is inversely proportional to r.

When $p = 8$, $q = 25$ and $r = 16$. Find the value of p when $r = 2$.

$p = $ ....
[Total 5 marks]

4 *a* is inversely proportional to *b*.
a is inversely proportional to c^2.

Show that *b* is directly proportional to c^2.

[Total 3 marks]

5 The density of an object, *d* g/cm³, is inversely proportional to its volume, *v* cm³.

If the volume of the object is increased by 40%, what is the percentage decrease in its density?
Give your answer to 1 decimal place.

Start by setting up equations for the densities of the object before and after the increase in volume.

.... %

[Total 4 marks]

6 *y* varies inversely with the square of *x*, as shown in the diagram on the right. *y* is also proportional to the cube of *z*.

When *x* = 2, *z* = 5. Calculate *y* when *z* = 15.

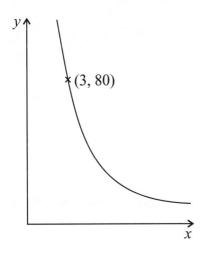

(3, 80)

....

[Total 5 marks]

Score:

27

Coordinates and Ratio

1   The line segment *AB* is shown below. *M* is the midpoint of *AB* and has coordinates (4, 5).

The coordinates of point *A* are (–2, 2).
a)   Find the coordinates of point *B*.

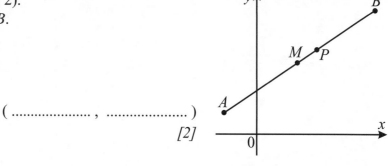

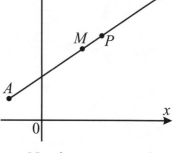

(.................... , ...)
                                                  [2]

Not drawn accurately

Point *P* lies on the line segment *AB* such that $MP:PB = 1:2$.
b)   Find the ratio $AP:AB$.

....
                                                  [3]

[Total 5 marks]

2   *ABCD* is a square with side length 4 units. The coordinates of point *D* are (2, –1).
M is the centre of the square and point *E* has coordinates (0, 5).

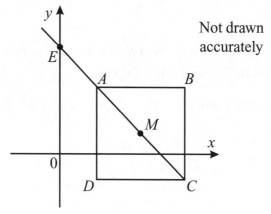

Not drawn accurately

Find the ratio $EM:MC$. Give your answer in its simplest form.

....
                                                  [Total 3 marks]

3 The diagram shows rectangle *ABCD*. Point *E* has coordinates (0, –4), point *F* has coordinates (6, 0) and point *B* has coordinates (6, 4).

Not drawn accurately

P is the point on the line *EB* such that *EP* : *PB* = 3 : 1. Calculate the length of the line segment *PF*.

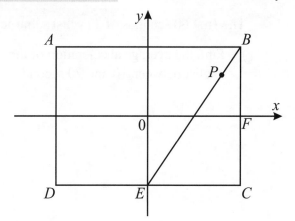

....

[Total 4 marks]

4 *ABCD* is a parallelogram. The coordinates of point *A* are (–2, 7) and the coordinates of point *D* are (–5, 2). *M* is the midpoint of line *AC* and has coordinates (3, 4.5).

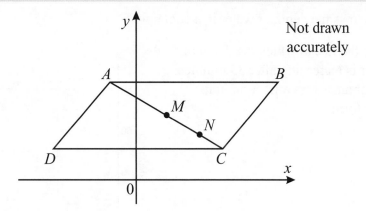

Not drawn accurately

Point *N* lies on the line *AC* such that *AM* : *MN* : *NC* = 5 : 3 : 2. Find the exact length *NB*.

....

[Total 6 marks]

Score:

18

Gradients

1 The first 60 seconds of a cyclist's journey are shown on the velocity-time graph below.

a) Find the average acceleration of the cyclist between 10 and 20 seconds.

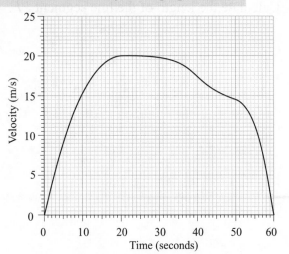

.... m/s²

[2]

b) Estimate the acceleration of the cyclist at 50 seconds. Give your answer to 3 s.f.

Draw a tangent to the curve at 50 seconds.

.... m/s²

[2]

[Total 4 marks]

2 The graph shows the depth of water in a container.

a) Estimate the rate at which the depth of the water is increasing after 35 minutes. Give your answer as a fraction in its simplest form.

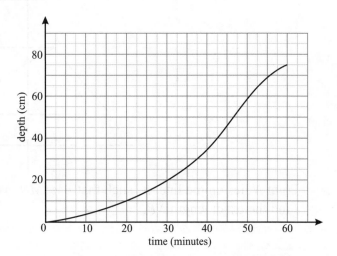

.... cm/min

[2]

b) Find the average rate at which the water increases over the 60 minute period.

.... cm/min

[2]

[Total 4 marks]

Score:

8

Perpendicular Lines

1 Line L_1 passes through the points (4, 6) and (11, 20).
Line L_2 is perpendicular to L_1 and intersects the x-axis at (28, 0).

Find the equation of line L_2.

....

[Total 3 marks]

2 The line SQ is a diagonal of the kite $PQRS$ and has equation $y = 4x - 3$.
The coordinates of point R are (8, 15). Find the equation of the other diagonal PR.

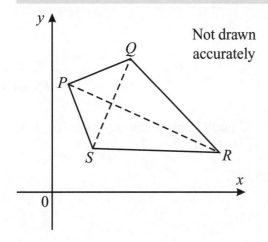

Not drawn
accurately

....

[Total 3 marks]

3 Lines L_1 and L_2 are perpendicular and intersect at point M.
L_1 has equation $x + 5y = 100$ and L_2 passes through point (2, 4).

Find the coordinates of point M.

(...................., ...)

[Total 5 marks]

Section Three — Graphs, Functions and Calculus

4 The line L_1 has equation $2y - x = 14$ and passes through the points $P(6, 10)$ and Q. L_2 is the line that is perpendicular to L_1 and passes through point P. L_2 intercepts the y-axis at R. RQ is horizontal.

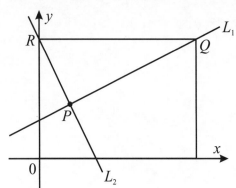

Find the coordinates of Q.

Not drawn accurately

(.................... , ...)

[Total 5 marks]

5 Lines L_1 and L_2 are parallel. L_1 has equation $2x + 3y = 12$ and L_2 passes through point $(6, 13)$. Line L_3 is perpendicular to L_1 and L_2 and intersects L_1 at $(3, 2)$.

Find the coordinates of the point of intersection of L_2 and L_3.

(.................... , ...)

[Total 6 marks]

Exam Practice Tip

Remember — the gradients of two perpendicular lines multiply to give −1. Once you know that, use whatever information you're given to find the equation of the line. You sometimes have to do quite a bit of work to find the equation, so if you're asked to find a point, don't forget to do the final step and find the coordinates.

Score

22

Section Three — Graphs, Functions and Calculus

Harder Graphs

1 The graph shows the curve $y = \dfrac{9}{x}$.

Find the smallest possible distance
between the two sections of the graph.
Give your answer as a simplified surd.

The closest points will
lie on the line $y = x$.

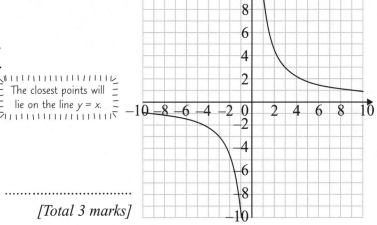

....

[Total 3 marks]

2 This question is about the equation $y = \dfrac{1}{x^2} - x + 3$.

a) Complete the table and draw the graph of $y = \dfrac{1}{x^2} - x + 3$ on the grid below.

x	y
-2	5.25
-1.5	
-1	
-0.5	
-0.2	28.2
0.2	27.8
0.5	
1	
1.5	
2	1.25

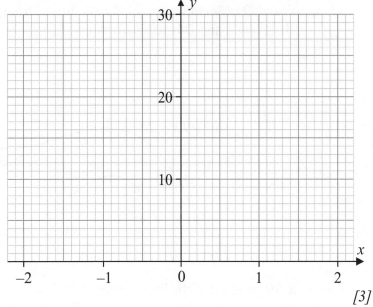

[3]

b) By drawing a straight line on your graph, estimate the solutions to $\dfrac{1}{x^2} - 6x - 9 = 0$ to 1 d.p.

....

[3]

c) $\dfrac{1}{x^2} - x - a = 0$ only has one solution.
Use your graph to explain why the maximum integer value of a is 1.

....

....

[2]

[Total 8 marks]

Section Three — Graphs, Functions and Calculus

3   The graph of the curve $y = x^2 - x - 4$ is shown.
      Use the graph to estimate the solutions to $x^2 + x = 1$.

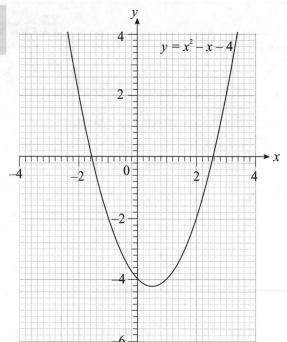

$x = $ ....

$x = $ ....

[Total 4 marks]

4   The graph shows the curves $y = ax^3 - bx + 2a$ and $y = 2ax^3 - 4ax - 2b$.
      The curve $y = ax^3 - bx + 2a$ passes through $A(-1, 5)$ and $B(2, 14)$.
      Points C and D lie on the curve $y = 2ax^3 - 4ax - 2b$, so that C is
      vertically below A and D is vertically below B.

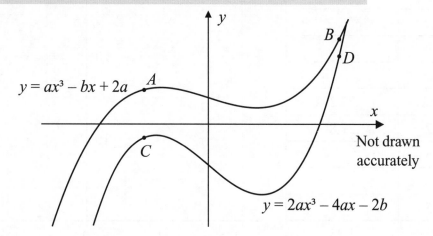

Calculate the gradient of the line segment CD.

....

[Total 7 marks]

Score: ☐

22

Section Three — Graphs, Functions and Calculus

Trig Graphs

1   The graph of $y = -\cos x$ is shown below for $0° \leq x \leq 360°$.

As shown on the graph,
$-\cos 75° = -0.259$.

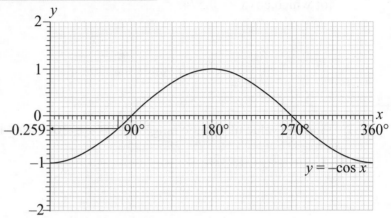

Give another value of x, found on this graph, where $-\cos x = -0.259$.

$x =$ ....$°$

[Total 1 mark]

2   The diagram shows a sketch of $y = \tan x$ for $0° \leq x \leq 360°$.

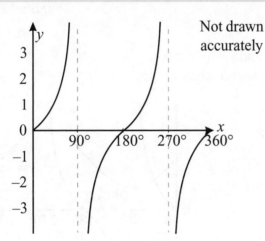

Not drawn
accurately

$\tan 105° = -3.732$.

Write down the two solutions to the equation $\tan x = 3.732$ for $0° \leq x \leq 360°$.

$x =$ ....$°$ and $x =$ ....$°$

[Total 2 marks]

3   The graphs of $y = \sin x$ and $y = \sin 2x$ for $0° \leq x \leq 360°$ are shown below.

For the graph of $y = \sin 2x + 3$,
find the x-value when $y = \dfrac{6 + \sqrt{2}}{2}$

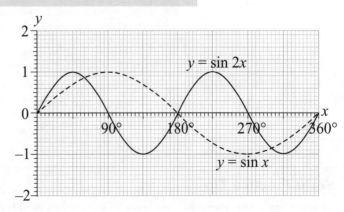

$y =$ ....

[Total 2 marks]

4 The diagram shows a sketch of $y = \cos x$ for $0° \leq x \leq 180°$.

As shown on the graph, $\cos 55° = 0.574$.

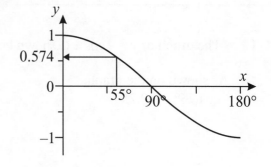

a) Find the value of x in the range $0° \leq x \leq 180°$ for which $\cos x = -0.574$.

$x = $ ....°
[1]

b) Find the value of x in the range $180° \leq x \leq 360°$ for which $\cos x = -0.574$.

$x = $ ....°
[1]

c) Find the value of x in the range $-180° \leq x \leq 0°$ for which $\cos x = 0.574$.

$x = $ ....°
[1]

[Total 3 marks]

5 The sketch below shows the graphs of $y = \tan x$ and $y = -\sin x + c$, where c is a positive number. The two graphs intersect when $x = 45°$.

The point $(90°, a)$ lies on the curve $y = -\sin x + c$.
Work out the value of a, give your answer to 2 d.p.

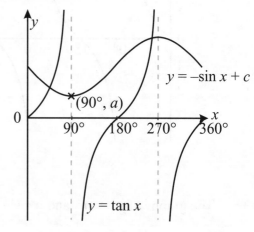

Not drawn accurately

$a = $ ....
[Total 3 marks]

Exam Practice Tip

It's really, really important that you know all the properties of the sin, cos and tan graphs — their shapes, where they cross the x- and y-axes, any symmetry they have, where the pattern repeats etc. If you're not given the graph over a big enough range to solve the question, you can always draw a quick sketch to help you.

Score

11

Functions

1 $f(x) = \sqrt{2x - 8}$ $(x \geq 4)$ and $g(x) = x^2 + 4$.

a) Find the exact value of fg(4). Give your answer in its simplest form.

....

[2]

b) Find gf(x).

gf(x) = ...

[2]

c) Find the inverse function $f^{-1}(x)$.

$f^{-1}(x) =$ ....

[3]

[Total 7 marks]

2 $f(x) = 2x - 1$ and $g(x) = \sin x$.

a) Find both solutions to the equation fg(x) = 0 for $0° \leq x \leq 360°$.

A quick sketch of the graph of y = sin x
will help you find the second x-value.

$x =$ ....° and $x =$ ....°

[4]

b) Write down the range of gf(x).

.... $\leq$ gf(x) $\leq$ ....

[1]

[Total 5 marks]

Section Three — Graphs, Functions and Calculus

3 $f(x) = \dfrac{x+5}{2}$ and $g(x) = 3x - 10$.

Find the value of x for which $f^{-1}(x) = g^{-1}(x)$.

$x =$ ....
[Total 6 marks]

4 $f(x) = x^2 + 4x + 3$ and $g(x) = x + 2$.

a) Find $fgg(x)$.

$fgg(x) =$ ....
[3]

b) Solve the equation $fgg(x) = 0$.

$x =$ .... or $x =$ ....
[2]
[Total 5 marks]

5 $f(x) = \dfrac{4x}{x+9}$ $(x \neq -9)$ and $g(x) = 2x + 1$.

a) Solve the equation $fg(x) = x$.

$x =$ .... or $x =$ ....
[5]

b) Write down the domain of $fg(x)$.

....
[1]
[Total 6 marks]

Exam Practice Tip

Don't be put off if you have to solve things in function questions. Just put in the expression you know for the function (you might have to work it out first if it's a composite or inverse function), then solve it like a normal equation. And in composite functions, always remember to do the function closest to x first.

Score

29

Section Three — Graphs, Functions and Calculus

Graph Transformations

1 The diagram shows a sketch of $y = f(x)$, which crosses the x-axis at -4 and 1, and has a turning point at $(-3, 4)$.

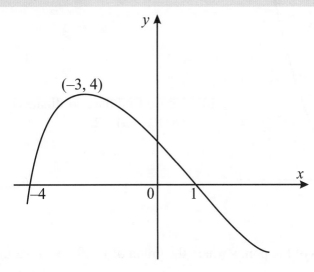

a) On the same axes, sketch the graph of $y = f(-x)$, labelling the turning point and where it crosses the x-axis.

[3]

b) Write down the coordinates of the turning point of $y = f(x + 3) + 2$.

(..................... , ...)

[2]

[Total 5 marks]

2 The diagram below shows the graph of $y = x^3 + 3x^2 + 2$.

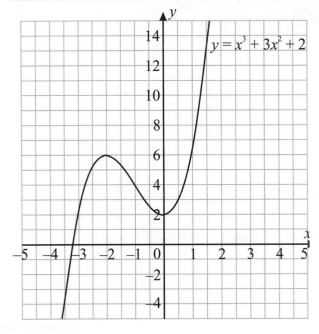

a) On the same axes, draw the graph of $y = (x - 3)^3 + 3(x - 3)^2 + 1$, showing clearly the coordinates of any turning points.

[3]

b) Expand and simplify $(x - 3)^3 + 3(x - 3)^2 + 1$.

....

[4]

[Total 7 marks]

Section Three — Graphs, Functions and Calculus

3   The diagram shows a sketch of $y = f(x)$, where $f(x) = x^2 - 5x + 7$.

a)   Find the coordinates of the turning point of f(x).

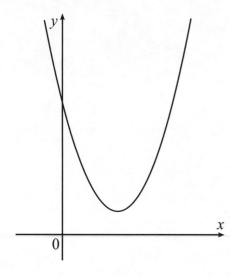

(..................... , ...)

[3]

b)   Hence find the coordinates of the turning point of
       $y = f(x + 3) - 2$.

(..................... , ...)

[2]

c)   Find the x-values of the points where the graph of $y = f(x + 3) - 2$ intersects the x-axis.

$x = $ .... and $x = $ ....

[3]

[Total 8 marks]

4   The graph $y = \dfrac{6}{x}$ is transformed into the graph of $y = \dfrac{3x}{x - 2}$.

a)   Show that $\dfrac{ab}{x - a} + b = \dfrac{bx}{x - a}$.

[2]

b)   Describe the transformation that maps the graph of $y = \dfrac{6}{x}$ to the graph of $y = \dfrac{3x}{x - 2}$.

....

....

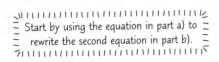
Start by using the equation in part a) to
rewrite the second equation in part b).

[3]

[Total 5 marks]

Score:

25

Section Three — Graphs, Functions and Calculus

Differentiation

1 The graph of $y = 5x^2 + 15x + 3$ has a gradient of a when $x = 4$.

Find the coordinates of the point on the graph that has a gradient of $-a$.

(.................. , ...)
[Total 5 marks]

2 Find the coordinates of the turning point of the curve with equation $y = 4x - \dfrac{5}{x^2}$.

Give your answers to 2 d.p.

> Rewrite the fraction in terms of a negative power of x.

(.................. , ...)
[Total 5 marks]

3 The function $y = x^3 + bx^2 - 2$, where b is a constant, has a turning point when $x = -2$.

a) Work out the value of b.

$b = $ ....
[4]

b) (i) Find the coordinates of the other turning point.

(..................... , ...)
[2]

(ii) Is this turning point a minimum or maximum? Explain your answer.

....

....

....
[2]
[Total 8 marks]

4 The height of an object above the ground, h metres, after t seconds can be roughly modelled by the equation $h = -2t^3 + 11t^2 - 16t + 7$ for $0 \leq t \leq 3.5$.

After how many seconds will the object first be moving away from the ground at 4 m/s?

.... seconds

[Total 6 marks]

5 A farmer wants to fence off a triangular piece of land so that the base length is $4x + 1$ km and the vertical height is $6 - 2x$ km.

a) Find the lower and upper bounds for x. Give your answer as an inequality.

.... $< x <$ ....

[2]

b) Find the maximum possible area that the farmer could fence off.

.... km²

[5]

[Total 7 marks]

6 The displacement, s metres, of a tennis ball from the net after t seconds can be modelled by the equation $s = -t^2 - \dfrac{4}{t} + 20$, where $0.2 \leq t \leq 5$.

Find the time at which the tennis ball is decelerating at 3 m/s².

.... seconds

[Total 6 marks]

Exam Practice Tip

Often in differentiation questions you'll just need to differentiate an equation, set it equal to 0 and solve. But sometimes you'll then have to substitute the value you found back into the original equation. So make sure you keep track of what you're working out and what the question is actually asking you for.

Score

37

Section Three — Graphs, Functions and Calculus

Circle Geometry

1   The diagram shows triangle *ABC*, where *A*, *B* and *C* are points on the circumference of a circle. *AB* = *AC*, and *DE* is a tangent to the circle at *C*.

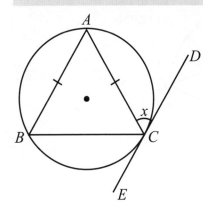

Angle *DCA* = *x*. *DE* is parallel to *AB*.
Prove that *ABC* is an equilateral triangle.
Give geometrical reasons to support the statements you make.

[Total 4 marks]

2   The diagram below shows the circle with centre *O*.
A, *B*, *C* and *D* are points on the circumference of the circle.

Find the size of angle *CDO*.

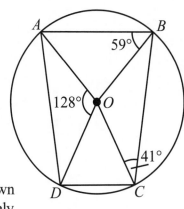

Not drawn accurately

CDO = ...°

[Total 4 marks]

3   The diagram shows a circle. *A*, *B*, *C*, *D* and *E* are points on the circumference of the circle. *DM* = 3 cm, *CM* = 4 cm, *AM* = 8 cm and *FE* = 14 cm.

Find the length of *FA*.
Give your answer to 3 significant figures.

Not drawn accurately

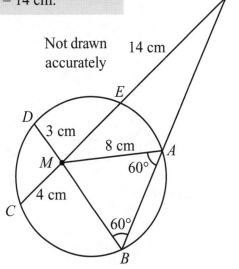

.... cm

[Total 6 marks]

4   The diagram below shows two intersecting circles with centres *O* and *P*. The circles intersect at *C* and *E*. *A*, *B* and *F* are points on the circumference with centre *O*, and *D* is a point on the circumference of the circle with centre *P*. *BD* and *DF* are straight lines.

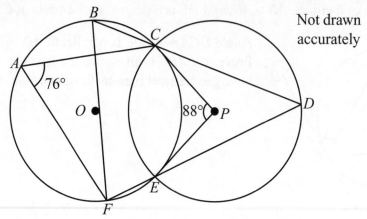

Not drawn accurately

Find the size of angle *BFE*. Give reasons for each step of your working.

BFE = ...°

[Total 3 marks]

5   Points *A*, *B*, *C* and *D* are points on the circumference of the circle below. *EF* is a tangent that meets the circle at *D*, and *AC* and *BD* are straight lines.

Show that *X* is NOT the centre of the circle.

Not drawn accurately

[Total 4 marks]

6 The diagram shows a circle with centre *O*. *B*, *C*, *E* and *F* are points on the circumference of the circle. *AB* and *AF* are tangents to the circle, and *BD* and *DF* are straight lines.

Find the size of angle *CDE*.

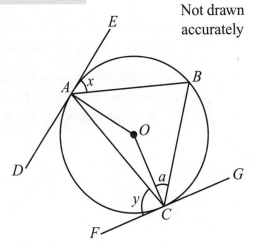

Not drawn accurately

CDE = ...°

[Total 5 marks]

7 The diagram shows a circle with centre *O*.
DE is a tangent to the circle at *A* and *FG* is a tangent to the circle at *C*.

Prove that $a = x + y - 90°$.
State any circle theorems that you use.

Not drawn accurately

[Total 4 marks]

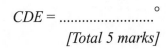

Exam Practice Tip

It's not always easy to spot which circle theorems you need to use — so just go through them one by one until you find one that works. There are usually one or two you can discount straight away (for example, if there are no tangents on the diagram, you probably aren't going to need the theorems that involve tangents).

Score

30

Section Four — Geometry and Measures

Enlargement

1 Three cylinders are mathematically similar. Their radii are in the ratio $1:3:5$.
The smallest cylinder has a vertical height of 6 cm.

a) Write down the ratio of the surface areas of the three cylinders.

....
[1]

b) The volume of the largest cylinder is 6750π cm^3.
Find the radius of the middle cylinder.

.... cm
[3]

[Total 4 marks]

2 An Egyptian pyramid has a volume of 2.5×10^6 m^3.
A museum is building a scale model of the pyramid.

a) The model has a volume of 160 m^3.
Find the scale factor used for the model.
Give your answer as a fraction in its simplest form.

The model is smaller than the original pyramid, so the scale factor will be less than 1.

....
[2]

b) The surface area of the model is 200 m^2.
What is the surface area of the original pyramid? Give your answer in standard form.

.... m^2
[2]

[Total 4 marks]

Section Four — Geometry and Measures

3 Two cones are mathematically similar. Cone A has a volume of 324π cm³ and cone B has a volume of 768π cm³. The surface area of cone A is 216π cm².

a) Find the exact surface area of cone B.

.... cm²

[2]

b) Write down the ratio of the radius of cone A to the radius of cone B.
Give your answer in its simplest form.

....

[1]

[Total 3 marks]

4 Cuboids A and B below are similar, and cuboid A has dimensions as shown.
The scale factor of enlargement from A to B is $\frac{8}{5}$.

1.5 cm   A   5 cm
2.5 cm   Not drawn accurately

a) Find the volume of cuboid B.

.... cm³

[2]

b) The cuboids are made out of different types of metal and both have a mass of 0.06 kg.
Find the percentage decrease in density from cuboid A to cuboid B.
Give your answer to 3 significant figures.

.... %

[3]

[Total 5 marks]

Section Four — Geometry and Measures

5 Will buys a set of three vases. The vases are mathematically similar and have bases with areas of 90 cm², 160 cm² and 1440 cm². The volume of the largest vase is 0.016 m³ and the height of the medium vase is 20 cm.

Find the height and volume of the smallest vase.

height = ... cm

volume = ... cm³

[Total 4 marks]

6 Anna makes necklaces using spherical beads. She has two different sizes of beads. Small beads have a volume of 2.4 cm³ and large beads have a volume of 8.1 cm³.

The time taken to decorate a bead is proportional to the surface area of the bead.
It takes 8 minutes to decorate a small bead.
She uses 5 small beads and 4 large beads to make a necklace.

Can she decorate all the beads needed for a necklace in $1\frac{3}{4}$ hours?
Show how you worked out your answer.

[Total 4 marks]

Exam Practice Tip

Just remember — for a scale factor of n, side lengths are n times bigger, areas (or surface areas) are n² times bigger and volumes are n³ times bigger. If you have a fractional scale factor, don't forget to square and cube both the numerator and denominator of the fraction to find the area and volume of the enlarged shape.

Score

24

Arcs, Sectors and Segments

1   The major sector on the right has an area of 88π cm^2.

Find the size of angle x.

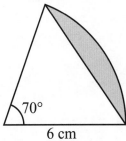

12 cm

$x = $ ....$^\circ$

[Total 3 marks]

2   The diagram on the right shows a sector of a circle.

a)   Find the area of the shaded segment. Give your answer to 3 s.f.

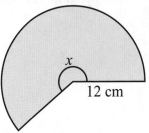

70°

6 cm

.... cm^2

[3]

b)   Find the perimeter of the shaded segment. Give your answer to 3 s.f.

You need to use the cosine rule for part b).

.... cm

[4]

[Total 7 marks]

3   A circle of radius 8 cm is divided up into equal sectors.
The perimeter of each sector is 21.6 cm to 3 s.f.

How many sectors are there in total?

....

[Total 3 marks]

4 Hannah cuts a slice of cake. The cake has a radius of 10 cm, and Hannah's slice is a sector with angle 45°. The cake is covered in two different colours of icing, as shown below.

a) Find the area of white icing on Hannah's slice of cake.
Give your answer to 3 s.f.

Not drawn accurately

.... cm²
[3]

10 cm

45°

5 cm   3 cm   2 cm

b) The height of the cake is 8 cm. Find the volume of Hannah's slice.
Give your answer to 3 s.f.

.... cm³
[2]

[Total 5 marks]

5 The diagram shows sector *ABC* of a circle with centre *C* and sector *DEF* of a circle with centre *F*. The diagram has a vertical line of symmetry, and *D* is the midpoint of *AC*.

DF = 1.6 cm, angle *DFE* = 140° and angle *DCE* = 60°.

a) By considering triangle *DFC*, calculate the length of *DC*.
Give your answer to 3 s.f.

You'll have to use
the sine rule here.

.... cm
[3]

A   *B*

D   140°   *E*

1.6 cm *F*

60°   Not drawn
C   accurately

b) Calculate the perimeter of the shaded region *ADEB*. Give your answer to 3 s.f.

.... cm
[5]

[Total 8 marks]

Score:

26

Section Four — Geometry and Measures

3D Shapes — Surface Area and Volume

1   Find the volume of the triangular prism below.
Give your answer to 3 significant figures.

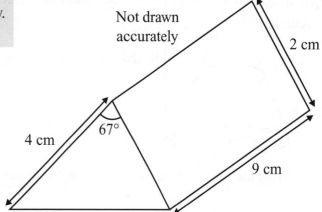

Not drawn
accurately

2 cm

4 cm

67°

9 cm

.... cm^3

[Total 3 marks]

2   The cone below has a volume of $(3.2 \times 10^{26})\pi$ m^3 and a radius of 4×10^8 m.
Find x, the vertical height of the cone. Give your answer in standard form.

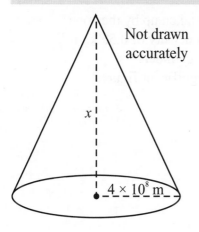

Not drawn
accurately

x

4×10^8 m

The formula for the volume of
a cone is $V = \frac{1}{3} \times \pi r^2 \times h_v$

.... m

[Total 3 marks]

3   Sphere A has radius 6 cm. The volume of sphere B is 60% greater
than the volume of sphere A. What is the radius of sphere B?

Give your answer to 3 significant figures.

The formula for the volume
of a sphere is $V = \frac{4}{3}\pi r^3$.

.... cm

[Total 4 marks]

4   A cone has radius 15 cm and height 36 cm. The top of the cone is removed
to create a new shape which is two-thirds of the height of the original cone.

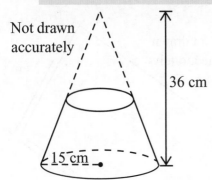

Not drawn
accurately

36 cm

15 cm

a)   Find the exact volume of the new shape.

.... cm³
[3]

b)   Find the exact surface area of the new shape.

.... cm²
[3]

[Total 6 marks]

5   A piece of apparatus for an experiment is made up of a cone within a cylinder.
The cone and cylinder have the same radius, and the vertical height of the cone
is the same as the vertical height of the cylinder (as shown in the diagram).

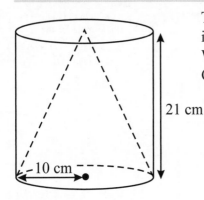

21 cm

10 cm

Not drawn accurately

The space within the cylinder not taken up by the cone
is filled with a gas. The gas has a density of 0.52 kg/m³.
What is the mass of the gas in the cylinder?
Give your answer in grams to 3 significant figures.

Be careful with the units here.

.... g
[Total 6 marks]

6   A flood channel is built to divert excess water from a river. The flood
channel is the shape of a triangular prism. When the flood is strongest, the
channel is full of water, which flows at a rate of 90 000 litres per minute.

Find the speed of the water in m/s.

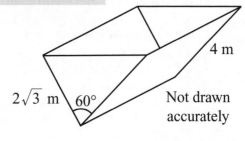

$2\sqrt{3}$ m   60°   4 m

Not drawn
accurately

.... m/s
[Total 5 marks]

7   A sphere with radius 1.4 m is cut into 8 identical pieces,
as shown below. The weight of the whole sphere is 5000 N.

One piece of the sphere is resting on horizontal ground on one of the flat faces.
Find the pressure exerted on the ground. Give your answer to 3 significant figures.

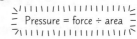
Pressure = force ÷ area

1.4 m

.... N/m²

[Total 4 marks]

8   The diagram shows a solid object made up of a hemisphere of radius $3k$ cm and a cone
with vertical height $4k$ cm. The total surface area of the object is 3993π cm².

Work out the value of k.

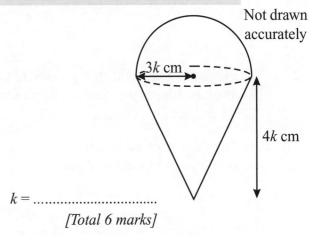

Not drawn
accurately

$3k$ cm

$4k$ cm

$k =$ ....

[Total 6 marks]

9   Josie melts down 1200 cm³ of steel. She uses 30% of the steel to make two identical spheres.
She uses $\frac{1}{3}$ of the steel to make four identical cones with the same radius as the spheres.

Work out whether Josie has enough steel left to make one cube
with side length equal to the height of the cone.

[Total 6 marks]

Score:

43

Section Four — Geometry and Measures

Trigonometry

1   The diagram below shows a large rhombus made up from four smaller rhombuses.

Show that the area of the large rhombus is $4n^2\sin\theta$ cm².

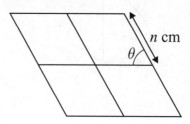

[Total 3 marks]

2   The diagram on the right shows a kite *ABCD*.
Diagonal *AC* bisects the diagonal *BD* at *O*.
$AO = 4$ cm and $OC = 10$ cm.

Calculate the size of angle *BAD*.
Give your answer to 1 decimal place.

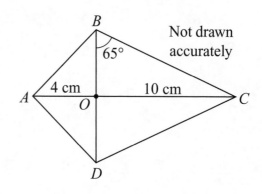

.........................°

....
[Total 3 marks]

3   The diagram below shows two mountains that have peaks at *A* and *B*.
$AO = 4$ km, $OD = 2$ km, angle $AOC = 60°$ and angle $BOD = 55°$.

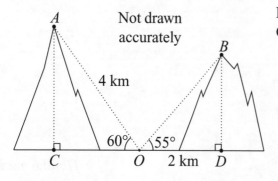

Find the angle of depression from *A* to *B*.
Give your answer to 1 decimal place.

.........................°

....
[Total 4 marks]

4   The diagram shows two right-angled triangles, *ABC* and *BCD*, and a semicircle.

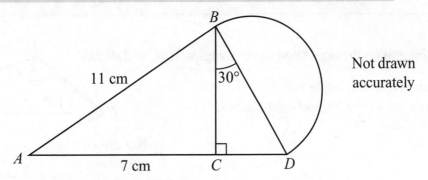

Not drawn accurately

AB = 11 cm, AC = 7 cm and angle CBD = 30°.
Calculate the area of the semicircle. Give your answer to 1 decimal place.

.... cm²

[Total 4 marks]

5   *A, B, C* and *D* are points on a circle. *EF* is a tangent to the circle at *C*.

AC is a diameter of the circle. EC = 4 cm.
Angle BEC = 58° and angle DAC = 53°.
a)   Find the area of the circle. Give your answer to 2 d.p.

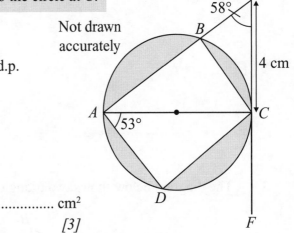

Not drawn accurately

.... cm²
[3]

b)   Find the total area of the shaded parts of the circle. Give your answer to 2 d.p.

.... cm²
[5]

[Total 8 marks]

Score: ☐

22

Section Five — Pythagoras and Trigonometry

The Sine and Cosine Rules

1 The diagram on the right shows two triangles, *ABC* and *ACD*.

Calculate the size of angle *x*.
Give your answer to 3 significant figures.

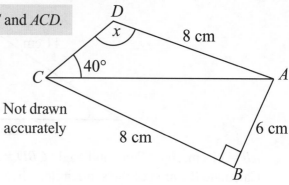

Not drawn accurately

.... °

[Total 4 marks]

2 The diagram on the right shows Peng's sketch of a patio design.

Work out the size of angle *ADC* in Peng's sketch.
Give your answer to 1 decimal place.

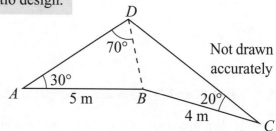

Not drawn accurately

.... °

[Total 5 marks]

3 The diagram below shows two triangles, *ABC* and *DEF*.

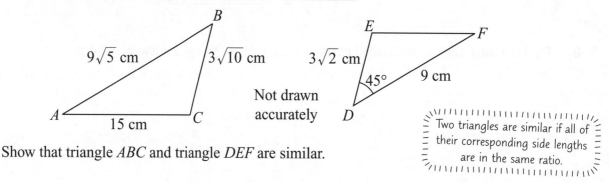

Not drawn accurately

Two triangles are similar if all of their corresponding side lengths are in the same ratio.

Show that triangle *ABC* and triangle *DEF* are similar.

[Total 4 marks]

4   Points *A*, *B*, *C* and *D* are points on the
circumference of a circle with centre *O*.
DC = 18 cm, angle *DOC* = 74° and angle *AOB* = 26°.

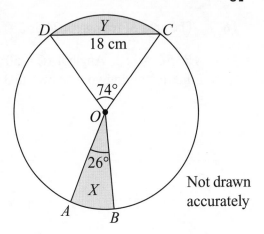

Not drawn
accurately

Work out which shaded area, *X* or *Y*, is bigger.
Show your working.

....
[Total 6 marks]

5   *ABCDE* is an irregular pentagon.

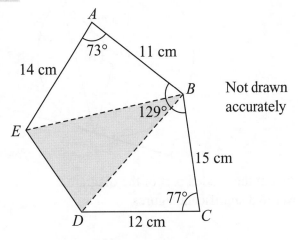

Not drawn
accurately

What is the area of triangle *BED*? Give your answer to 3 significant figures.

.... cm²
[Total 5 marks]

6 The area of triangle *ABC* is 38 cm².

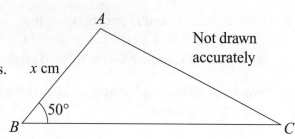

Not drawn accurately

AB : BC = 1 : 2. Angle *ABC* = 50°.
Find *AC*, giving your answer to 3 significant figures.

.... cm

[Total 4 marks]

7 *A* and *B* are points on a circle with centre *O*.
CD is a tangent to the circle at *A* and *CE* is a tangent to the circle at *B*.

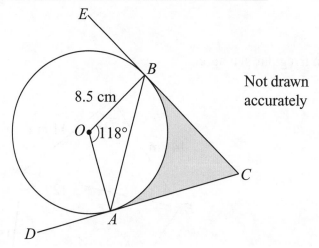

Not drawn accurately

Calculate the area of the shaded part of the diagram.
Give your answer to 3 significant figures.

Find the area of the minor segment, then subtract it from the area of triangle ABC.

.... cm²

[Total 7 marks]

Score:

35

Section Five — Pythagoras and Trigonometry

3D Pythagoras and Trigonometry

1   The solid on the right is made from two identical cones
joined at their bases. The slant height of each cone is
4.2 m and the overall vertical height of the solid is 6 m.

Work out the volume of the solid.
Give your answer to 3 significant figures.

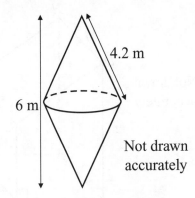

4.2 m

6 m

Not drawn
accurately

.... m³
[Total 3 marks]

2   The diagram shows a pyramid with a rectangular base. The vertex, *V*,
of the pyramid is directly above the centre of the base *ABCD*.

VC = 8.9 cm, *VX* = 7.2 cm and *BC* = 4.2 cm.
Work out the length *AB*. Give your answer to 3 significant figures.

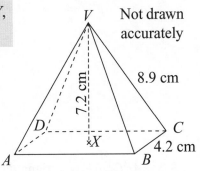

V   Not drawn
accurately

7.2 cm

8.9 cm

D

X

C

4.2 cm

A

B

.... cm
[Total 4 marks]

3   The base of the pyramid *ABCDEFV* is a regular hexagon with side length 8 cm.
The vertex, *V*, of the pyramid is directly above the centre of the base, *X*.

The height *VX* of the pyramid is 15 cm.

Calculate the angle between the plane *VED* and
the base *ABCDEF*. Give your answer to 1 decimal place.

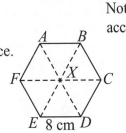

A   *B*

Not drawn
accurately

F   *X*   *C*

E   8 cm   *D*

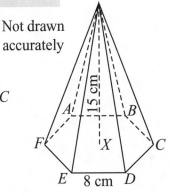

V

15 cm

A   *B*

F   *X*   *C*

E   8 cm   *D*

°
....
[Total 3 marks]

4   The diagram shows a prism *ABCDEFGH*.
    ABFE is a square, and *M* and *N* are the midpoints of *DH* and *BF* respectively.

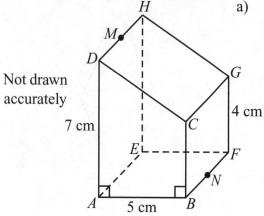

a)   Calculate the angle between the line *HB* and the base *ABFE*.
    Give your answer to 3 significant figures.

Not drawn accurately

.........................°

[3]

b)   Calculate angle *BMF*. Give your answer to 3 significant figures.

.........................°

[3]

[Total 6 marks]

5   *ABCDEF* is a triangular prism.

A is vertically above *B* with *AB* = 4 cm.
BC = 8 cm and *CF* = 12 cm.
N is the point on *AD* such that *AN* : *ND* = 3 : 1.

Calculate the angle *CNF*.
Give your answer to 1 decimal place.

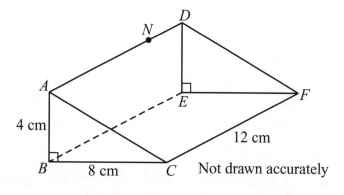

.........................°

[Total 5 marks]

Exam Practice Tip

A good approach when you're tackling a 3D trigonometry question is to break it down into triangles —
sketch the triangles, label their vertices, then label any lengths or angles that you know from the 3D shape.
Then just use 2D trig on your triangles. The same method applies to 3D Pythagoras questions.

Score

21

Section Five — Pythagoras and Trigonometry

Vectors

1 *ABCD* is a parallelogram. $\overrightarrow{LA} = \mathbf{a}$, $\overrightarrow{AM} = \mathbf{b}$,
M is the midpoint of *AB* and the ratio *AL* : *LD* is 1 : 3.

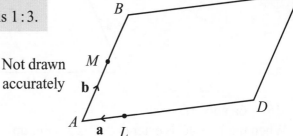

Given that $\mathbf{a} = \begin{pmatrix} -3 \\ -1 \end{pmatrix}$ and $\mathbf{b} = \begin{pmatrix} 2 \\ 4 \end{pmatrix}$,
calculate the magnitude of $\overrightarrow{CA}$.

Not drawn
accurately

....

[Total 4 marks]

2 *ABCD* is a parallelogram.

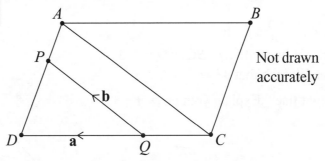

Not drawn
accurately

$\overrightarrow{QP} = \mathbf{b}$ and $\overrightarrow{QD} = \mathbf{a}$. Triangles *PQD* and *ACD* are similar and *AD* : *PD* = 5 : 3

a) Find $\overrightarrow{CA}$ in terms of **a** and **b**.

....

[1]

R is a point on *AC* such that $5\overrightarrow{AR} = 2\overrightarrow{AC}$.

b) Given that $\overrightarrow{PR} = k\overrightarrow{DQ}$, find the value of *k*.

k = ...

[3]

[Total 4 marks]

Section Five — Pythagoras and Trigonometry

3   *ABCD* is a parallelogram.

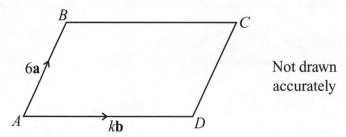

$\overrightarrow{AB} = 6\mathbf{a}$ and $\overrightarrow{AD} = k\mathbf{b}$.

When the line *AC* is extended, *E* is a point on *AC* such that $\overrightarrow{BE} = 4\mathbf{a} + 25\mathbf{b}$.

Calculate the value of *k*.

k = ...

[Total 4 marks]

4   The shape below is made up of two triangles, *ABF* and *BCF*, and a parallelogram *CDEF*.

$\overrightarrow{AB} = 3\mathbf{a}$ and $\overrightarrow{AF} = \dfrac{15}{4}\mathbf{a} + 2\mathbf{b}$.

ABCD is a straight line with $AB : BC : CD = 4 : 3 : 4$.

M is a point on *CF* such that $4\overrightarrow{FM} = \overrightarrow{MC}$.

Is *AME* a straight line? Explain your answer.

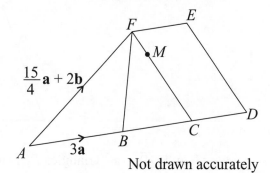

[Total 5 marks]

Score:

Comparing Data Sets

1   27 people were asked to rate website A
    and website B out of ten. The ratings
    for website A had a median of 7 and
    an interquartile range of 5. The ratings
    of website B are shown in the diagram.

    Using information from the chart,
    compare the ratings of the two websites.

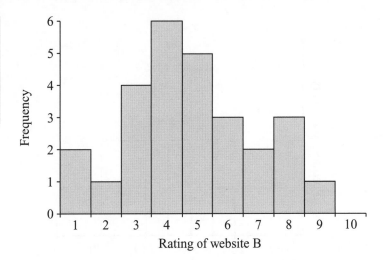

....

....

....

....

....

[Total 4 marks]

2   This cumulative frequency graph shows
    how quickly tickets for a pantomime
    sold out in 2013. The table below
    summarises how quickly tickets for
    the same pantomime sold out in 2014.

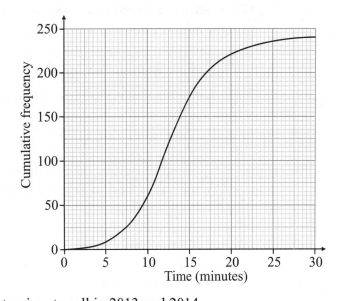

Ticket Sales in 2014	
Time it took to sell out	24 minutes
Median	16 minutes
Interquartile range	3 minutes

Compare the times it took tickets for the pantomime to sell in 2013 and 2014.

....

....

....

....

....

[Total 4 marks]

3 The house prices of three-bedroom houses in two towns, A and B, are shown in the histograms.

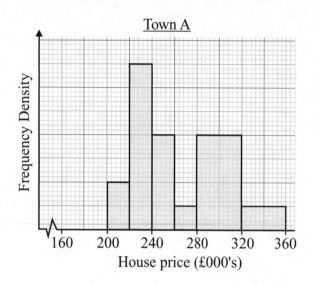

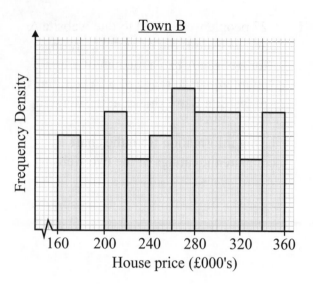

a) Decide whether each of these statements is correct. Give reasons for your answers.
   (i) "There is a greater range of three-bedroom house prices in town A."

   ....

   ....

   ....

   [2]

   (ii) "There are more three-bedroom houses priced between £320 000 and £360 000 in town B than town A."

   ....

   ....

   ....

   [2]

b) Is there a higher proportion of three-bedroom houses between £280 000 and £320 000 in town A or town B? Show working to support your conclusion.

   [4]

   [Total 8 marks]

   Score: ⬚

   16

Histograms

1   A cycling club decided to measure how long it took each of its members to complete a 1 km course. 39 members took between 70 and 85 seconds to complete the course.

The histogram on the right shows the times recorded by the members.
How many members does the cycling club have?

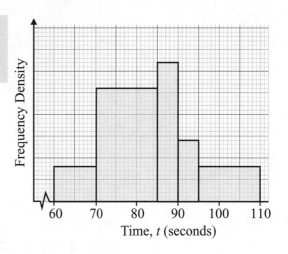

....

[Total 4 marks]

2   A sample of 600 bouncy balls were individually weighed and the results are shown on the histogram below.

a)   Estimate the mean weight of the bouncy balls.
Give your answer to 1 d.p.

> Find the frequencies of each class by working out the proportion of the graph that each bar takes up.

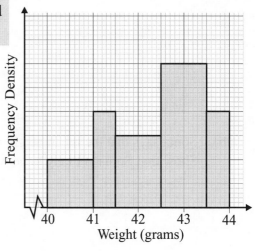

.... g

[5]

b)   Sumi says, "The median weight of the bouncy balls is over 42.5 g."
Is she correct? Explain your answer.

....

....

[2]

[Total 7 marks]

Section Six — Statistics and Probability

3 The histogram shows the heights of the statues in a palace.

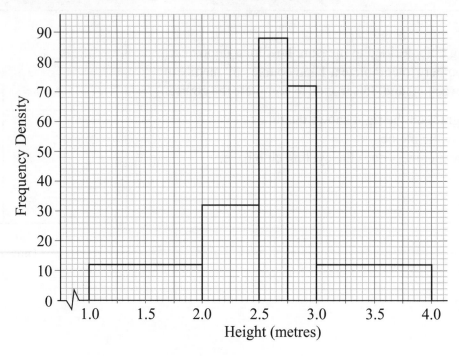

a) Work out an estimate for the percentage of statues that have a height between 1.75 metres and 2.75 metres.

.... %
[3]

b) Sonia says that the mean height of the statues is less than 2.5 metres.
    Show that Sonia is likely to be wrong.

[3]

c) What is the probability that a randomly chosen statue is over 3 metres tall, given that it's over 2 metres tall?

....
[2]

[Total 8 marks]

Score:

19

Probability

1　The table below shows the results of rolling a dice 200 times.

Number	1	2	3	4	5	6
Frequency	54	12	38	9	61	26

a)　What is the relative frequency of rolling an odd number? Give your answer as a decimal.

....

[2]

b)　Desmond says, "If I roll the dice I am likely to get a 5." Criticise Desmond's statement.

....

....

[1]

[Total 3 marks]

2　Anya spins a spinner that has four sections numbered 1-4.
She is three times as likely to spin a 1 as to spin a 3.
She is twice as likely to spin an even number as an odd number.

a)　What is the probability that she spins a 3?

....

[2]

b)　What is the probability that, in two spins, she gets one even number and one odd number?

....

[2]

c)　Is Anya more likely to spin an odd number on her first spin or three even numbers in a row?
Show working to explain your answer.

....

....

....

....

[2]

[Total 6 marks]

3   At a school, there are two Year 9 classes, A and B. Each class contains 30 students.
Mrs Dawson randomly selects one student from each class.
The probability that she selects a girl from class A (G_A) and a girl from class B (G_B) is 0.24.
The probability that she selects a girl from class A (G_A) and a boy from class B (B_B) is 0.56.

How many girls are there in Year 9?

Form two simultaneous equations —
remember that P(boy) = 1 − P(girl).

....

[Total 4 marks]

4   Jill has two bags containing blue and red balls.

Bag A	**Bag B**
14 blue	n blue
n red	30 red

When two blue balls are taken from Bag A and placed into Bag B,
the probability of picking a red ball is the same for both bags.

Show that the original probability of picking a red ball from Bag B is $\frac{5}{8}$.

[Total 6 marks]

Score:

19

Section Six — Statistics and Probability

Tree Diagrams

1   A card is chosen at random from a standard pack of 52 cards.
It is then replaced and another card is chosen at random.

a)   Complete the tree diagram below. Give probabilities as fractions in their simplest form.

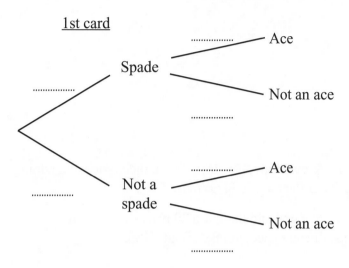

b)   What is the probability that the first card is not a spade and the second card is not an ace?
Give your answer as a fraction in its simplest form.

....

[1]

[Total 3 marks]

2   A fair 12-sided dice numbered 1-12 is rolled three times.

a)   What is the probability that all three rolls produce prime numbers?
Give your answer as a fraction in its simplest form.

....

[2]

b)   What is the probability that exactly one of the numbers is less than 5?
Give your answer as a fraction in its simplest form.

....

[3]

[Total 5 marks]

3   Mark is fishing for mackerel. He has 2 hooks on his line, so each time he casts his line he can catch either 0, 1 or 2 mackerel. On any cast, the probability that he catches 0 mackerel is 0.2, 1 mackerel is 0.5 and 2 mackerel is 0.3.

What is the probability that in 3 casts he catches less than 5 fish?

> Hint: P(less than 5 fish)
> = 1 – P(5 or more fish).

....

[Total 4 marks]

4   A game at a fund-raising event involves throwing a dice twice and adding the scores together. The player wins a prize if the total is 11 or more.

a)   It costs £2 to play the game and there are 20 prizes to be won.
Explain why the stall can expect to take about £480.

[3]

b)   Pablo plays the game twice. Find the probability than he wins at least one prize.
Give your answer as a fraction.

....

[3]

[Total 6 marks]

5   The probability that Martyn goes to aerobics any evening is 0.4. If he doesn't go to aerobics, the probability that he goes for a run the next morning is 0.7. The probability that he goes to aerobics and goes for a run the next morning is 0.25.

Use a tree diagram to calculate the probability that he doesn't go for a run.

....

[Total 3 marks]

Section Six — Statistics and Probability

6 In a tombola there are 100 tickets numbered 1-100.
You win a prize if you pick a ticket that ends in 0 or 5.

a) Amy is the first person to play and picks two tickets at random.
What is the probability that she wins at least one prize?

....

[4]

b) Carla plays after 40 tickets have been chosen and 5 prizes have been won.
She picks two tickets at random. Are her chances of winning at least one prize
better or worse than Amy's? Explain your answer.

....

....

....

....

....

[3]

[Total 7 marks]

7 A bag contains counters that are either green or blue.
  • There are n green counters.
  • The number of blue counters is one more than the number of green counters.
Two counters are taken out of the bag at random without replacement.

Show that the probability that both counters are the same colour is $\dfrac{n}{2n+1}$.

[Total 5 marks]

Exam Practice Tip

Even when questions don't mention tree diagrams, it's often a good idea to draw one so that you
don't make any silly mistakes. If you're feeling confident, you don't need to draw the whole diagram
— just draw the branches that you think you'll need to be able to answer the question.

Score

33

Section Six — Statistics and Probability

Probability from Venn Diagrams

1 The universal set ξ is the integers 1-20.

Set A is made up of the numbers generated by the sequence $2n + 1$ where n is a positive integer.

Set B is made up of the numbers generated by the sequence $\dfrac{n(n+1)}{2}$ where n is a positive integer.

a) Complete this Venn diagram to show the number of elements in each set.

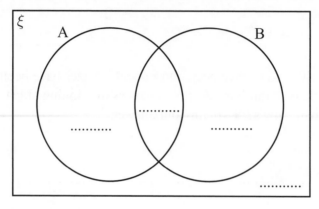

[3]

b) What is the probability that a randomly chosen element is in both set A and set B?

....

[1]

[Total 4 marks]

2 The Venn diagram on the right shows the number of students at a school who attended the school disco (D) and chess club (C).

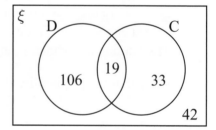

a) What is the ratio of students attending the disco to the total number of students? Give your answer in its simplest form.

....

[2]

b) What is the probability that a randomly chosen student
(i) attended chess club, given that they also went to the school disco?

....

[2]

(ii) attended the disco, given that they only attended one event?

....

[2]

[Total 6 marks]

3 Jack asked 80 people whether they like baking, running and shopping.
Half of the people only liked one activity. 10% of people liked all three activities.
22 people liked baking and running. 18 people liked shopping and running.
43 people liked baking and 35 liked shopping. Everyone liked at least one activity.

a) Complete this Venn diagram to show the number of elements in each set.

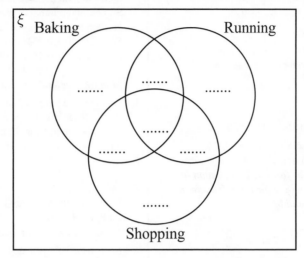

[5]

b) What is the probability that a randomly selected person liked baking, given that they liked at least two activities? Give your answer as a fraction in its simplest form.

....

[2]

[Total 7 marks]

4 In the Venn diagram on the right,
ξ = 50 people in a choir
P = people who play the piano
G = people who play the guitar.

Two different people in the choir are chosen at random.
Find the probability that they can both play the piano.

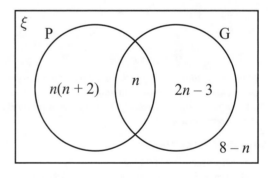

....

[Total 5 marks]

Score:

22

Answers

Section One — Numbers

Page 2: Fractions and Recurring Decimals

1 a) Let $r = 0.7\dot{5}$.

Then $100r = 75.7\dot{5}$.

So $99r = 75.7\dot{5} - 0.7\dot{5} = 75$ and $r = \dfrac{75}{99} = \dfrac{25}{33}$

[2 marks available — 1 mark for correct method for converting the recurring decimal to a fraction, 1 mark for the correct answer]

b) $\dfrac{a}{11} + \dfrac{b}{6} = \dfrac{6a + 11b}{66}$

$\dfrac{25}{33} = \dfrac{50}{66}$, so $\dfrac{6a + 11b}{66} = \dfrac{50}{66}$ and $6a + 11b = 50$

$11b$ could be 11, 22, 33 or 44, so $6a$ could be 39, 28, 16 or 6.

Only 6 is multiple of 6, so $a = 1$ and $11b = 44 \Rightarrow b = 4$

[3 marks available — 1 mark for forming an equation in a and b, 1 mark for a correct method for finding a and b, 1 mark for correct values of a and b]

2 a) Let $r = 0.\dot{2}$.

Then $10r = 2.\dot{2}$, so $9r = 2.\dot{2} - 0.\dot{2} = 2$ and $r = \dfrac{2}{9}$.

$2.\dot{2} = 2\dfrac{2}{9} = \dfrac{20}{9}$ cm

[2 marks available — 1 mark for a correct method for converting the recurring decimal to a fraction, 1 mark for the correct answer]

b) Area of one tile $= \left(\dfrac{20}{9}\right)^2 = \dfrac{400}{81}$ cm² *[1 mark]*

Heather will need $1600 \div \dfrac{400}{81} = 324$ tiles *[1 mark]*

[2 marks available in total — as above]

3 Let $r = 0.14\dot{2}$.

Then $1000r = 142.4\dot{2}$ and $10r = 1.4\dot{2}$.

$1000r - 10r = 142.4\dot{2} - 1.4\dot{2}$, so $990r = 141$

$r = \dfrac{141}{990} = \dfrac{47}{330}$, so $\dfrac{7x - 3}{6} = \dfrac{47}{330}$

$7x - 3 = \dfrac{47}{55}$

$7x = 3 + \dfrac{47}{55} = \dfrac{212}{55}$, so $x = \dfrac{212}{385}$

[4 marks available — 1 mark for a correct method for converting the recurring decimal to a fraction, 1 mark for a correct fraction, 1 mark for a correct method for solving the equation, 1 mark for the correct answer]

Pages 3-4: Percentages

1 1st quarter sales: £12 000 000

2nd quarter sales: £12 000 000 × 1.1 = £13 200 000

3rd quarter sales: £13 200 000 × 1.1 = £14 520 000

4th quarter sales: £14 520 000 × 1.1 = £15 972 000

Total sales = £12 000 000 + £13 200 000 + £14 520 000

  + £15 972 000 = £55 692 000

Profit = 28% of £55 692 000 = 0.28 × 55 692 000 = £15 593 760

Bonus = 30% of £15 593 760 = 0.3 × 15 593 760

  = £4 678 128 = £4 700 000 (2 s.f.)

[4 marks available — 1 mark for working out the sales in the 2nd, 3rd and 4th quarters, 1 mark for working out the total yearly sales, 1 mark for working out the profit for the year, 1 mark for the correct answer]

2 Simone scored 0.85 × 120 = 102 marks on exam A, and

  0.5 × 80 = 40 marks on exam B. *[1 mark for both]*

Let M be the total number of marks available on exam C,

then she scored $0.95M$ marks on exam C.

So her total number of marks was $102 + 40 + 0.95M$. *[1 mark]*

Her total number of marks was also $0.75 \times (120 + 80 + M)$

So $102 + 40 + 0.95M = 0.75(120 + 80 + M)$ *[1 mark]*

  $142 + 0.95M = 150 + 0.75M$

  $0.2M = 8$, so $M = 40$ *[1 mark]*

[4 marks available in total — as above]

3 Call the side length of cube $A = s$,

then side length of cube $B = 1.2s$ *[1 mark]*

Let P_A be the pressure of cube A, P_B be the pressure of cube B

and w be the weight of each cube.

Pressure $= \dfrac{\text{Force}}{\text{Area}}$, so $P_A = \dfrac{w}{s^2}$ so $w = P_A s^2$ *[1 mark]*

$P_B = \dfrac{w}{(1.2s)^2}$ so $w = 1.44 P_B s^2$ *[1 mark]*

Equating values of w gives: $P_A s^2 = 1.44 P_B s^2$, so $P_A = 1.44 P_B$

So P_A is 144% of P_B *[1 mark]*

[4 marks available in total — as above]

4 Each year, 10% is added to the customer's money

and the investment company takes $12 - 10 = 2\%$

The customer's money at the start of each year is:

Year 1 = £100 000, Year 2 = £100 000 × 1.1 = £110 000,

Year 3 = £110 000 × 1.1 = £121 000

And the investment company makes:

Year 1 = £100 000 × 0.02 = £2000,

Year 2 = £110 000 × 0.02 = £2200,

Year 3 = £121 000 × 0.02 = £2420

So the investment company makes £2000 + £2200 + £2420 = £6620

[5 marks available — 1 mark for a correct method to find the customer's money each year, 1 mark for the correct amounts of the customer's money, 1 mark for a correct method to find the investment company's money each year, 1 mark for the correct amounts of the company's money, 1 mark for the correct answer]

5 Let the number of houses in Liverstone be L, then the number of houses in Ashmouth is $1.7L$. *[1 mark]*

Expressions for the number of terraced houses in each village are:

Liverstone: $0.28L$ Ashmouth: $0.2 \times 1.7L$

So $(0.2 \times 1.7L) - 0.28L = 480$ *[1 mark]*

  $0.34L - 0.28L = 480$

  $0.06L = 480$, so $L = 8000$ *[1 mark]*

So there are 8000 houses in Liverstone, and

8000 × 1.7 = 13 600 houses in Ashmouth. *[1 mark]*

There are 8000 × 0.38 = 3040 semi-detached houses in Liverstone

and 13 600 × 0.4 = 5440 semi-detached houses in Ashmouth.

The difference in the number of semi-detached houses is

5440 – 3040 = 2400 *[1 mark]*

[5 marks available in total — as above]

Pages 5-6: Ratios

1 Speed = Distance ÷ Time

Speed of rowing boat = 18 ÷ 2.25 = 8 km/h

Speed of canoe = 8000 ÷ 0.5 = 16 000 m/h = 16 km/h

So the ratio of the speeds is 8 km/h : 16 km/h = 1 : 2

[4 marks available — 1 mark for finding the speed of the boat, 1 mark for finding the speed of the canoe, 1 mark for a ratio with both parts in the same units, 1 mark for the correct answer]

Make sure both speeds have the same units before you simplify the ratio.

2   Let triangle A have height x cm and base length y cm.
Then triangle B has height $x + 1$ cm and base length $3y$ cm.
The area of triangle B is 45 cm², so the area of
triangle A is $(45 \div 9) \times 2 = 10$ cm².
Triangle A: $\frac{1}{2} \times x \times y = 10$ so $xy = 20$ [1]

Triangle B: $\frac{1}{2} \times (x + 1) \times 3y = 45$, rearranging gives $xy + y = 30$ [2]

Substituting [1] into [2] gives: $20 + y = 30$ so $y = 10$
Put this value back into [1] to give $x = 2$.
Height of triangle $A = 2$ cm and height of triangle $B = 2 + 1 = 3$ cm.
So the ratio of vertical heights is $2 : 3$.
[5 marks available — 1 mark for setting up an equation for the
area of triangle A, 1 mark for setting up an equation for the area
of triangle B, 1 mark for a correct method to solve the equations
simultaneously, 1 mark for the correct vertical heights of each
triangle, 1 mark for the correct answer]

3   E.g. Say that Jenna has completed $x\%$ and Harvey has completed
$y\%$. Then $x : y = 3 : 4$ and $x + 7 : y + 7 = 7 : 9$.
$\frac{x}{y} = \frac{3}{4}$ and $\frac{x + 7}{y + 7} = \frac{7}{9}$
$4x = 3y$ and $9(x + 7) = 7(y + 7)$
$4x - 3y = 0$ [1] and $9x - 7y = -14$ [2]
$[1] \times 7$: $28x - 21y = 0$ [3], and $[2] \times 3$: $27x - 21y = -42$ [4]
$[3] - [4]$: $x = 42$, so she has completed 42% of the game.
[4 marks available — 1 mark for setting up two ratios in terms of
x and y and converting them to fractions, 1 mark for multiplying
out the fractions to form a pair of simultaneous equations,
1 mark for a correct method to solve the simultaneous equations,
1 mark for the correct answer]

4   $x - 10 : y - 10 = 2 : 5$ and $x + 8 : y + 8 = 1 : 2$.
$\frac{x - 10}{y - 10} = \frac{2}{5}$ and $\frac{x + 8}{y + 8} = \frac{1}{2}$
$5(x - 10) = 2(y - 10)$ and $2(x + 8) = y + 8$
$5x - 2y = 30$ [1] and $2x - y = -8$ [2]
$[2] \times 2$: $4x - 2y = -16$ [4]
$[1] - [3]$: $x = 46$
Substitute into [2] to find y: $(2 \times 46) - y = -8$ so $y = 100$
So x as a percentage of y is: $\frac{46}{100} \times 100 = 46\%$
[5 marks available — 1 mark for setting up two ratios in terms of
x and y and converting them to fractions, 1 mark for multiplying
out the fractions to form a pair of simultaneous equations,
1 mark for a correct method to solve the simultaneous equations,
1 mark for the correct values of x and y, 1 mark for the correct
answer]

5   Let the original number of red and green sweets in the bag be x.
Let the number of yellow sweets be y.
The numbers of red, yellow and green sweets remaining
are $x - 5$, $y - 15$ and $x - 25$ respectively.
red : yellow $= 2 : 3$ so $x - 5 : y - 15 = 2 : 3$
$\frac{x - 5}{y - 15} = \frac{2}{3}$
$3(x - 5) = 2(y - 15)$, so $3x - 2y = -15$ [1]
yellow : green $= 3 : 1$ so $y - 15 : x - 25 = 3 : 1$
$\frac{y - 15}{x - 25} = 3$
$y - 15 = 3(x - 25)$, so $3x - y = 60$ [2]
$[2] - [1]$: $y = 75$
Substituting back into [2] gives $3x - 75 = 60$, so $x = 45$
The total number of sweets originally in the bag is
$45 + 75 + 45 = 165$
The fraction that are yellow is $\frac{75}{165} = \frac{5}{11}$

[6 marks available — 1 mark for giving the number of red,
yellow and green sweet in terms of x and y, 1 mark for setting up
two ratios in terms of x and y and converting them to fractions,
1 mark for multiplying out the fractions to form a pair of
simultaneous equations, 1 mark for a correct method to solve the
simultaneous equations, 1 mark for the correct values of x and y,
1 mark for the correct answer]

Pages 7-8: Bounds

1   a) $4z^3 = \frac{\left(x^{\frac{1}{2}}y^{-3}z\right)^2}{y^{-5}} = \frac{xy^{-6}z^2}{y^{-5}} = xy^{-1}z^2$

$4z = \frac{x}{y}$, so $z = \frac{x}{4y}$

[3 marks available — 3 marks for the correct answer,
otherwise 1 mark for simplifying the powers on the
numerator, 1 mark for dividing both sides by z^2]

   b)   Upper bound for $x = 6.85$, lower bound for $y = 1.15$

Upper bound for $z = \frac{6.85}{4 \times 1.15} = 1.489... = 1.49$ (3 s.f.)

[3 marks available — 1 mark for finding the upper bound
of x, 1 mark for finding the lower bound of y, 1 mark
for the correct answer]

2   Maximum possible score without the vault:
upper bound $= 16.425 + 13.155 + 14.885 = 44.465$ *[1 mark]*
Lowest possible score of 2nd place $= 60.145$
Shannon's minimum score including the vault
$= 60.145 + 0.05 = 60.195$ *[1 mark]*
So lowest possible score for the vault
$= 60.195 - 44.465 = 15.73$ *[1 mark]*
[3 marks available in total — as above]

3   Lower bound for $c = 11.75$, upper bound for $a = 6.25$ *[1 mark]*
So lower bound for scale factor $= 11.75 \div 6.25 = 1.88$ *[1 mark]*
Lower bound for $b = 3.45$ *[1 mark]*
Lower bound for $d = 3.45 \times 1.88 = 6.486$ cm *[1 mark]*
[4 marks available in total — as above]

4   Lower bound for $S = 179.15$
Upper bound for $S = 179.25$ *[1 mark for both]*
Lower bound for $x = 59.5$
Upper bound for $x = 60.5$ *[1 mark for both]*

$S = \frac{x}{360} \times \pi r^2$, so $r^2 = \frac{360S}{x\pi}$ *[1 mark]*

Lower bound for r: $r^2 = \frac{360 \times 179.15}{60.5 \times \pi} = 339.323...$,

so $r = 18.420... = 18.42$ (2 d.p.) *[1 mark]*

Upper bound for r: $r^2 = \frac{360 \times 179.25}{59.5 \times \pi} = 345.219...$,

so $r = 18.580... = 18.58$ (2 d.p.) *[1 mark]*
[5 marks available in total — as above]

5   Lower bound for $A = 2850$, upper bound for $A = 2950$
Lower bound for $x = 96.95$, upper bound for $x = 97.05$
Lower bound for $y = 78.85$, upper bound for $y = 78.95$
[2 marks for all bounds correct, otherwise 1 mark for four or five
bounds correct]

Lower bound for θ: $\sin\theta = \frac{2 \times 2850}{97.05 \times 78.95} = 0.743...$

so $\theta = \sin^{-1}(0.743...) = 48.066...°$ *[1 mark]*

Upper bound for θ: $\sin\theta = \frac{2 \times 2950}{96.95 \times 78.85} = 0.771...$

so $\theta = \sin^{-1}(0.771...) = 50.515...°$ *[1 mark]*

Value of θ using the rounded values: $\sin\theta = \frac{2 \times 2900}{97.0 \times 78.9} = 0.757...$

so $\theta = \sin^{-1}(0.757...) = 49.274...°$ *[1 mark]*
Difference between lower bound and rounded value
$= 49.274... - 48.066... = 1.207...°$
Difference between upper bound and rounded value
$= 50.515... - 49.274... = 1.241...°$ *[1 mark for both]*
So maximum possible error $= 1.24°$ (3 s.f.) *[1 mark]*
[7 marks available in total — as above]

Page 9: Standard Form

1 Upper bound for weight = 4.25×10^4 = 42 500 N
Lower bound for area = 25 m^2
Upper bound for pressure = 42 500 ÷ 25 = 1700 N/m^2 > 1600 N/m^2, so it is not definitely safe for the shipping container to be transported on the cargo ship.
[3 marks available — 1 mark for finding the upper bound for weight and the lower bound for area, 1 mark for the upper bound for pressure, 1 mark for the conclusion]

2 Volume of salt in the Heron Sea = 12% of 1.4×10^{14}
= $0.12 \times 1.4 \times 10^{14}$ = 1.68×10^{13} litres *[1 mark]*
Volume of salt in the Cobalt Sea = 8% of 8.5×10^{12}
= $0.08 \times 8.5 \times 10^{12}$ = 6.8×10^{11} litres *[1 mark]*
Percentage decrease: $\dfrac{1.68 \times 10^{13} - 6.8 \times 10^{11}}{1.68 \times 10^{13}} \times 100$
= 95.952...% = 95.95% (2 d.p.) *[1 mark]*
[3 marks available in total — as above]

3 $a = 2^{10} \times 5^9$
$b = (3 \times 3) \times 10^6 = (3 \times 3) \times (2 \times 5)^6 = 2^6 \times 3^2 \times 5^6$ *[1 mark]*
$c = 24 \times 10^8 = 2 \times 2 \times 2 \times 3 \times (2 \times 5)^8 = 2^{11} \times 3 \times 5^8$ *[1 mark]*
LCM = $2^{11} \times 3^2 \times 5^9$ *[1 mark]* = $2^2 \times 3^2 \times (2 \times 5)^9 = 2^2 \times 3^2 \times 10^9$
= $36 \times 10^9 = 3.6 \times 10^{10}$ *[1 mark]*
[4 marks available in total — as above]

Page 10: Sets and Venn Diagrams

1 $n(F) = 15 = 3n + 2 + t + 2n$ so $13 = 5n + t$ [1] *[1 mark]*
$n(R) = 13 = t + 2n + n - 3t$ so $13 = 3n - 2t$ [2] *[1 mark]*
Substituting $t = 13 - 5n$ into [2] gives:
$13 = 3n - 2(13 - 5n)$
$13 = 3n - 26 + 10n$
$39 = 13n$ and so $n = 3$ *[1 mark]*
Putting in $n = 3$ into [1] gives $t = 13 - (5 \times 3) = -2$ *[1 mark]*
$n(F \cap R) = t + 2n = -2 + (2 \times 3) = 4$ *[1 mark]*
[5 marks available in total — as above]

2 a) $n(A \cup B) = 4 + 3 + 7 + 2 + 5 + 1 = 22$ *[1 mark]*
   b) $n(C) = 2 + 5 + 1 + 6 = 14$
       $n(C \cap (A' \cup B)) = 5 + 1 + 6 = 12$
       So $\dfrac{12}{14} = \dfrac{6}{7}$ of the elements in C are also in $A' \cup B$
       [2 marks available — 1 mark for finding either n(C) or n(C ∩ (A' ∪ B)) correctly, 1 mark for the correct answer]
   c) (i) $A' \cap B \cap C$ *[1 mark]*
       (ii) $A \cap B' \cap C$ or $A \cap B \cap C$ *[1 mark]*

Section Two — Algebra

Pages 11-13: Powers and Surds

1 $(\sqrt{5} - 6)^3 = (\sqrt{5} - 6)(\sqrt{5} - 6)(\sqrt{5} - 6)$
$= (5 - 6\sqrt{5} - 6\sqrt{5} + 36)(\sqrt{5} - 6)$
$= (41 - 12\sqrt{5})(\sqrt{5} - 6)$
$= 41\sqrt{5} - 246 - 60 + 72\sqrt{5} = 113\sqrt{5} - 306$
[3 marks available — 1 mark for expanding the first pair of brackets, 1 mark for expanding the new pair of brackets, 1 mark for the correct answer]

2 $a^7 \times (25a^6b^{10}c^5)^{\frac{1}{2}} = \sqrt{25}\, a^{(6 \div 2) + 7}b^{10 \div 2}c^{5 \div 2} = 5a^{10}b^5c^{\frac{5}{2}}$
[2 marks available — 2 marks for the correct answer, otherwise 1 mark for at least 2 of 5, a^{10}, b^5 or $c^{\frac{5}{2}}$ correct]

3 $\sqrt{343} = \sqrt{49 \times 7} = 7\sqrt{7}$ *[1 mark]*, $\dfrac{21}{\sqrt{7}} = \dfrac{21\sqrt{7}}{7} = 3\sqrt{7}$ *[1 mark]*
and $4\sqrt{252} = 4\sqrt{36 \times 7} = 24\sqrt{7}$ *[1 mark]*
So $\sqrt{343} + \dfrac{21}{\sqrt{7}} - 4\sqrt{252} = 7\sqrt{7} + 3\sqrt{7} - 24\sqrt{7}$
$= -14\sqrt{7}$ *[1 mark]*
[4 marks available in total — as above]

4 $\left(\dfrac{729}{8x}\right)^{\frac{1}{3}} = \dfrac{9}{4}$, so $8x = 4^3 = 64$ *[1 mark]*, which means $x = 8$ *[1 mark]*
[2 marks available in total — as above]

5 Volume = $\sqrt{5}(1 + \sqrt{5})(2 + 3\sqrt{5}) = (\sqrt{5} + 5)(2 + 3\sqrt{5})$
$= 2\sqrt{5} + 15 + 10 + 15\sqrt{5} = 25 + 17\sqrt{5}$ cm^3
[4 marks available — 1 mark for multiplying either bracket by $\sqrt{5}$, 1 mark for multiplying the result by the remaining bracket, 1 mark for correct expansion, 1 mark for the correct answer]

6 $b = (4c + 3)^{\frac{1}{3}}$, so $b^3 = (4c + 3)^{\frac{1}{3} \times 3} = 4c + 3$ *[1 mark]*
and $b^6 = (4c + 3)^2 = 16c^2 + 24c + 9$ *[1 mark]*
So $a = 3b^3 + 2b^6 = 3(4c + 3) + 2(16c^2 + 24c + 9)$
$= 12c + 9 + 32c^2 + 48c + 18 = 32c^2 + 60c + 27$ *[1 mark]*
[3 marks available in total — as above]

7 $\dfrac{2\sqrt{3}}{3 + \sqrt{3}} = \dfrac{2\sqrt{3}(3 - \sqrt{3})}{(3 + \sqrt{3})(3 - \sqrt{3})} = \dfrac{6\sqrt{3} - 6}{9 - 3} = \dfrac{6\sqrt{3} - 6}{6} = \sqrt{3} - 1$
$\dfrac{2 + \sqrt{3}}{2 - \sqrt{3}} = \dfrac{(2 + \sqrt{3})(2 + \sqrt{3})}{(2 - \sqrt{3})(2 + \sqrt{3})} = \dfrac{7 + 4\sqrt{3}}{4 - 3} = \dfrac{7 + 4\sqrt{3}}{1} = 7 + 4\sqrt{3}$
So $\dfrac{2\sqrt{3}}{3 + \sqrt{3}} + \dfrac{2 + \sqrt{3}}{2 - \sqrt{3}} = (\sqrt{3} - 1) + (7 + 4\sqrt{3}) = 6 + 5\sqrt{3}$
[5 marks available — 2 marks for correctly rationalising the denominator of the first fraction (or 1 mark for multiplying by $(3 - \sqrt{3})$), 2 marks for correctly rationalising the denominator of the second fraction (or 1 mark for multiplying by $(2 + \sqrt{3})$), 1 mark for the correct answer]

8 $\left(\dfrac{64}{49}\right)^{\frac{x}{y}} = \left(\dfrac{49}{64}\right)^{\frac{x}{y}} = \dfrac{343}{512}$, so $(\sqrt[y]{49})^x = 343$ and $(\sqrt[y]{64})^x = 512$
$\sqrt{49} = 7$ and $7^3 = 343$, and $\sqrt{64} = 8$ and $8^3 = 512$,
so $x = 3$ and $y = 2$
[3 marks available — 1 mark for inverting the fraction and making the power positive, 1 mark for forming two equations in terms of x and y, 1 mark for finding the values of x and y]

9 $(1 + 2\sqrt{2})^2 = (1 + 2\sqrt{2})(1 + 2\sqrt{2}) = 1 + 2\sqrt{2} + 2\sqrt{2} + 8$
$= 9 + 4\sqrt{2}$ *[1 mark]*
So $\dfrac{(1 + 2\sqrt{2})^2}{\sqrt{2} - 1} = \dfrac{9 + 4\sqrt{2}}{\sqrt{2} - 1} = \dfrac{(9 + 4\sqrt{2})(\sqrt{2} + 1)}{(\sqrt{2} - 1)(\sqrt{2} + 1)}$ *[1 mark]*
$= \dfrac{17 + 13\sqrt{2}}{2 - 1}$ *[1 mark]* = $17 + 13\sqrt{2}$ *[1 mark]*
[4 marks available in total — as above]

Pages 14-15: Quadratic Equations

1 Surface area of a sphere = $4\pi r^2$
$36\pi x^2 + 48\pi x + 16\pi = 4\pi(9x^2 + 12x + 4) = 4\pi(3x + 2)^2$
So $(3x + 2)^2 = r^2$, which means the radius is $(3x + 2)$ cm
[3 marks available — 1 mark for taking out a factor of 4π, 1 mark for factorising, 1 mark for square rooting to find the answer]

2 a) $2x^2 - 3x - 35 = (2x + 7)(x - 5)$
       [2 marks available — 1 mark for correct numbers in brackets, 1 mark for correct signs]
   b) $2(2x - 1)^2 - 3(2x - 1) - 35 = 0$
       $(2(2x - 1) + 7)((2x - 1) - 5) = 0$ *[1 mark]*
       $(4x + 5)(2x - 6) = 0$ *[1 mark]*,
       so $x = -1.25$ or $x = 3$ *[1 mark for both]*
       [3 marks available in total — as above]

3 $\dfrac{x}{2x + 1} - \dfrac{x + 3}{x - 1} = 2$
$x(x - 1) - (x + 3)(2x + 1) = 2(x - 1)(2x + 1)$
$x^2 - x - 2x^2 - x - 6x - 3 = 2(2x^2 + x - 2x - 1)$
$-x^2 - 8x - 3 = 4x^2 - 2x - 2$
$0 = 5x^2 + 6x + 1 = (5x + 1)(x + 1)$, so $x = -0.2$ or $x = -1$
[4 marks available — 1 mark for multiplying through by $(x - 1)(2x + 1)$, 1 mark for expanding brackets and rearranging to give a quadratic in the standard format, 1 mark for factorising, 1 mark for both correct answers]

4 a) $3x^2 - 14x - 24 = (3x+4)(x-6)$
   [2 marks available — 1 mark for correct numbers in brackets, 1 mark for correct signs]
   b) $3x^2 - 14x - 24 = (3x+4)^2$
   $(3x+4)(x-6) = (3x+4)^2$
   $(3x+4)(x-6) - (3x+4)^2 = 0$ *[1 mark]*
   $(3x+4)[(x-6) - (3x+4)] = 0$
   $(3x+4)(-2x-10) = 0$ *[1 mark]*
   So $x = -\dfrac{4}{3}$ *[1 mark]* or $x = -5$ *[1 mark]*
   [4 marks available in total — as above]
   Don't be tempted to cancel a factor of (3x + 4) from each side of the equation — you'd only end up with one solution instead of two.

5 Surface area of a cylinder = $2\pi rh + 2\pi r^2$
   So $2\pi r + 2\pi r^2 = 31\pi$ (as $h = 1$) *[1 mark]*
   $2r^2 + 2r - 31 = 0$ *[1 mark]*
   $r = \dfrac{-2 \pm \sqrt{2^2 - (4 \times 2 \times -31)}}{2 \times 2} = \dfrac{-2 \pm \sqrt{252}}{4}$ *[1 mark]*
   $= \dfrac{-2 \pm 6\sqrt{7}}{4} = \dfrac{-1 \pm 3\sqrt{7}}{2}$
   The radius must be positive, so $r = \dfrac{-1 + 3\sqrt{7}}{2}$ m *[1 mark]*.
   [4 marks available in total — as above]
   You're asked for the exact value of r, so leave your answer in surd form.

6 $\dfrac{1}{x} + \dfrac{6}{x+2} = 5$, so $x + 2 + 6x = 5x(x+2)$
   $7x + 2 = 5x^2 + 10x$
   $0 = 5x^2 + 3x - 2 = (5x-2)(x+1)$, so $x = \dfrac{2}{5}$ or $x = -1$
   $\dfrac{1}{1-3x}$ is positive when $x = -1$, so $\dfrac{1}{1-3(-1)} = \dfrac{1}{4}$.
   [5 marks available — 1 mark for multiplying through by x(x + 2), 1 mark for expanding brackets and rearranging to give a quadratic in the standard form, 1 mark for factorising, 1 mark for both correct values of x, 1 mark for the correct answer]

Page 16: Completing the Square

1 $7 \div 2 = \dfrac{7}{2}$, so $a = \dfrac{7}{2}$ and the brackets are $\left(x + \dfrac{7}{2}\right)^2$ *[1 mark]*.
   Expanding the brackets: $\left(x + \dfrac{7}{2}\right)^2 = x^2 + 7x + \dfrac{49}{4}$ *[1 mark]*
   To complete the square: $11 - \dfrac{49}{4} = -\dfrac{5}{4}$, so $b = -\dfrac{5}{4}$ *[1 mark]*
   So $x^2 + 7x + 11 = \left(x + \dfrac{7}{2}\right)^2 - \dfrac{5}{4}$.
   [3 marks available in total — as above]

2 $r(x+4)^2 + t = rx^2 + 8rx + 16r + t$
   Equating coefficients with $3x^2 + sx + 29$ gives $3x^2 = rx^2$,
   so $r = 3$ *[1 mark]*. $sx = 8rx$, so $s = 8r = 8 \times 3 = 24$ *[1 mark]*.
   $29 = 16r + t$, so $t = 29 - (16 \times 3) = -19$ *[1 mark]*.
   $y = 3(x+4)^2 - 19$ has a turning point at $(-4, -19)$ *[1 mark]*.
   [4 marks available in total — as above]

3 a) Dividing the first two terms by 5: $5(x^2 + 4x) + 12$
   $4 \div 2 = 2$, so the first bit is $5(x+2)^2$
   Expanding brackets gives: $5(x+2)^2 = 5(x^2 + 4x + 4)$
   $= 5x^2 + 20x + 20$
   To complete the square: $12 - 20 = -8$
   So $5x^2 + 20x + 12 = 5(x+2)^2 - 8$
   [4 marks available — 1 mark for dividing the first two terms by 5, 1 mark for finding the value of v, 1 mark for finding the value of w, 1 mark for the fully correct answer]
   b) $5x^2 + 20x + 12 = 0$
   So $5(x+2)^2 - 8 = 0$
   $(x+2)^2 = \dfrac{8}{5}$
   $x + 2 = \pm\sqrt{\dfrac{8}{5}}$, so $x = -2 \pm \sqrt{\dfrac{8}{5}}$
   $x = -0.735$ (3 s.f.) or $x = -3.26$ (3 s.f.)
   [2 marks available — 1 mark for rearranging the completed square, 1 mark for both correct x-values]

Pages 17-18: Algebraic Fractions

1 $\dfrac{2v^2 - 18}{v^2 + 3v} \times \dfrac{v^2 - v}{v^2 + 8v - 9} = \dfrac{2(v+3)(v-3)}{v(v+3)} \times \dfrac{v(v-1)}{(v+9)(v-1)}$
   $= \dfrac{2(v-3)}{v+9}$
   [5 marks available — 1 mark for factorising each of the numerators and denominators, 1 mark for the correct answer]

2 $\dfrac{1}{a} \div \dfrac{1}{b} = \dfrac{1}{a} \times b = \dfrac{1}{5x^2 - 80y^2} \times (40y - 10x)$
   $= \dfrac{10(4y-x)}{5(x+4y)(x-4y)} = \dfrac{-10(x-4y)}{5(x+4y)(x-4y)} = \dfrac{-2}{x+4y}$
   [4 marks available — 1 mark for multiplying by b, 1 mark for factorising a, 1 mark for factorising b, 1 mark for the correct answer]
   Here you had to spot that (4y − x) = −1 × (x − 4y).

3 $\dfrac{3}{x} + \dfrac{2x}{x+4} = \dfrac{3(x+4) + x(2x)}{x(x+4)} = \dfrac{2x^2 + 3x + 12}{x(x+4)}$
   [3 marks available — 1 mark for putting over a common denominator, 1 mark for adding numerators, 1 mark for correctly simplifying]

4 $\dfrac{x+7}{x^2} \times \dfrac{x^2 + 2x}{x^2 - 49} \times \dfrac{6x - 42}{3x + 6}$
   $= \dfrac{x+7}{x^2} \times \dfrac{x(x+2)}{(x+7)(x-7)} \times \dfrac{6(x-7)}{3(x+2)} = \dfrac{2}{x}$
   [5 marks available — 1 mark for factorising each of the numerators and denominators of the second and third fractions, 1 mark for the correct answer]

5 $\dfrac{1}{x^2} + \dfrac{x+3}{x-2} - \dfrac{4}{x} = \dfrac{(x-2) + x^2(x+3) - 4x(x-2)}{x^2(x-2)}$
   $= \dfrac{x - 2 + x^3 + 3x^2 - 4x^2 + 8x}{x^2(x-2)} = \dfrac{x^3 - x^2 + 9x - 2}{x^2(x-2)}$
   [4 marks available — 1 mark for multiplying top and bottom of the first fraction by (x − 2), 1 mark for multiplying top and bottom of the second fraction by x^2, 1 mark for multiplying top and bottom of the third fraction by x(x − 2), 1 mark for simplifying]

6 $\dfrac{x^2 - 5}{2x^2 - 7x - 4} \times \dfrac{2x + 1}{x - \sqrt{5}} = \dfrac{(x+\sqrt{5})(x-\sqrt{5})}{(2x+1)(x-4)} \times \dfrac{2x+1}{x-\sqrt{5}} = \dfrac{x+\sqrt{5}}{x-4}$
   [3 marks available — 1 mark for correctly factorising x^2 − 5, 1 mark for factorising the denominator of the first fraction, 1 mark for the correct answer]

7 $\dfrac{14x - 35}{2x^2 + x - 15} \div \dfrac{4xy - 12y}{2x^2y - 18y} = \dfrac{14x - 35}{2x^2 + x - 15} \times \dfrac{2x^2y - 18y}{4xy - 12y}$
   $= \dfrac{7(2x-5)}{(2x-5)(x+3)} \times \dfrac{2y(x+3)(x-3)}{4y(x-3)}$
   $= \dfrac{7}{2}$, so $\dfrac{14x - 35}{2x^2 + x - 15} \div \dfrac{4xy - 12y}{2x^2 - 18y} = k$, where $k = \dfrac{7}{2}$
   [6 marks available — 1 mark for inverting the second fraction and multiplying, 1 mark for factorising each of the numerators and denominators, 1 mark for the value of k]

Pages 19-20: Quadratic Inequalities

1 $x^2 + x - 56 = 0$ factorises to give $(x+8)(x-7) = 0$. The graph of $y = x^2 + x - 56$ is a u-shaped quadratic that crosses the x-axis at $x = -8$ and $x = 7$, and the graph is below 0 between these points. So $-8 < x < 7$.
   [3 marks available — 1 mark for factorising the quadratic to find the solutions, 1 mark for −8 and 7, 1 mark for correct inequality symbols]
   Sketching a graph is always handy when solving quadratic inequalities.

2    $4x - x^2 = 0$ factorises to give $x(4 - x) = 0$, so $4x - x^2 \leq 0$ means
     $x \leq 0$ and $x \geq 4$.

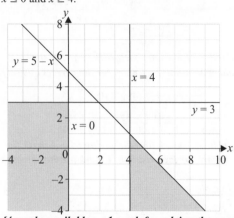

[4 marks available — 1 mark for solving the quadratic inequality,
1 mark for drawing the lines $x = 0$, $x = 4$ and $y = 3$, 1 mark for
drawing the line $y = 5 - x$, 1 mark for shading the correct regions]

3   Area of circle A = πr^2 cm²
     Area of circle B = $\pi(3r)^2$ cm² = $9\pi r^2$ cm²
     Sum of areas = $\pi r^2 + 9\pi r^2 = 10\pi r^2$ cm², so $10\pi r^2 > 160\pi$
     $r^2 > 16$ so $r < -4$ or $r > 4$
     r cannot be negative so $r > 4$. The smallest possible integer value
     of r is 5, so the smallest possible radius of circle A is 5 cm and the
     smallest possible radius of circle B is $3 \times 5 = 15$ cm.
     [3 marks available — 1 mark for finding an expression for the
     sum of the areas, 1 mark for forming an inequality for the areas
     and solving to find r, 1 mark for the correct radius of both circles]

4    $3x^2 - x - 90 \geq 5x + 15$, so $3x^2 - 6x - 105 \geq 0$
     Solve the quadratic equation $3x^2 - 6x - 105 = 0$
     $x^2 - 2x - 35 = 0$
     $(x + 5)(x - 7) = 0$
     The graph of $y = 3x^2 - 6x - 105$ is a u-shaped quadratic that crosses
     the x-axis at $x = -5$ and $x = 7$, and the graph is above 0 when $x \leq -5$
     and $x \geq 7$.
     [4 marks available — 1 mark for rearranging the inequality,
     1 mark for factorising the quadratic to find the solutions,
     1 mark for –5 and 7, 1 mark for correct inequality symbols]

5   a)   The volume of cuboid A is $3x(x + 2) = 3x^2 + 6x$ cm³. *[1 mark]*
         The volume of cuboid B is $4x^2$ cm³. *[1 mark]*
         $3x^2 + 6x < 4x^2$ so $x^2 - 6x > 0$. *[1 mark]*
         [3 marks available in total — as above]
     b) $x^2 - 6x = 0$ factorises to give $x(x - 6) = 0$ *[1 mark]*.
         The graph of $y = x^2 - 6x$ is a u-shaped quadratic that crosses
         the x-axis at $x = 0$ and $x = 6$, and the graph is positive (i.e. > 0)
         when $x < 0$ and $x > 6$ *[1 mark]*.
         The smallest positive integer solution is $x = 7$ *[1 mark]*,
         so the smallest possible volume of cuboid B is
         $4 \times 7 \times 7 = 196$ cm³. *[1 mark]*
         [4 marks available in total — as above]

6    $x^2 \leq \dfrac{23x - 45}{2}$, so $2x^2 \leq 23x - 45$, which means $2x^2 - 23x + 45 \leq 0$.
     $2x^2 - 23x + 45 = 0$ factorises to give $(2x - 5)(x - 9) = 0$. The graph
     of $y = 2x^2 - 23x + 45$ is a u-shaped quadratic that crosses the x-axis
     at $x = 2.5$ and $x = 9$, and the graph is below 0 between these points.
     So $2.5 \leq x \leq 9$.
     [4 marks available — 1 mark for rearranging the inequality,
     1 mark for factorising the quadratic to find the solutions,
     1 mark for 2.5 and 9, 1 mark for correct inequality symbols]

Pages 21-22: Simultaneous Equations

1    $2x - y = x + 4$, so $x = y + 4$
     Then $(y + 4)^2 + 4y^2 = 37$ *[1 mark]*
     $y^2 + 8y + 16 + 4y^2 = 37$
     $5y^2 + 8y - 21 = 0$ *[1 mark]*
     $(5y - 7)(y + 3) = 0$ *[1 mark]*, so $y = 1.4$ or $y = -3$ *[1 mark]*
     When $y = 1.4$, $x = 1.4 + 4 = 5.4$
     When $y = -3$, $x = -3 + 4 = 1$
     So the solutions are $x = 5.4$, $y = 1.4$ and $x = 1$, $y = -3$ *[1 mark]*
     [5 marks available in total — as above]

2   Area = $(2x \times x) + (y \times 3y) = 2x^2 + 3y^2$
     So $2x^2 + 3y^2 = 83$
     Base length = $2x + y$, so $2x + y = 9$, which means $y = 9 - 2x$
     So $2x^2 + 3(9 - 2x)^2 = 83$
     $2x^2 + 243 - 108x + 12x^2 = 83$
     $14x^2 - 108x + 160 = 0$
     $7x^2 - 54x + 80 = 0$, so $(7x - 40)(x - 2) = 0$
     So $x = 40 \div 7 = 5.714...$ or $x = 2$. x is an integer so $x = 2$.
     When $x = 2$, $y = 9 - 2(2) = 9 - 4 = 5$.
     [5 marks available — 1 mark for forming equations for the area
     and base length, 1 mark for substituting an expression for x or y
     into the quadratic equation, 1 mark for factorising the quadratic
     equation, 1 mark for the correct value of x, 1 mark for the correct
     value of y]

3    $7x - y = 25$, so $y = 7x - 25$
     Then $x^2 + (7x - 25)^2 = 25$ *[1 mark]*
     $x^2 + 49x^2 - 350x + 625 = 25$
     $50x^2 - 350x + 600 = 0$
     $x^2 - 7x + 12 = 0$
     $(x - 3)(x - 4) = 0$ *[1 mark]*, so $x = 3$ or $x = 4$ *[1 mark]*
     When $x = 3$, $y = (7 \times 3) - 25 = 21 - 25 = -4$
     When $x = 4$, $y = (7 \times 4) - 25 = 28 - 25 = 3$
     So the line intersects the circle at $(3, -4)$ and $(4, 3)$ *[1 mark]*
     Change in $x = 4 - 3 = 1$, change in $y = 3 - (-4) = 7$ *[1 mark for both]*
     Length $AB = \sqrt{1^2 + 7^2} = \sqrt{50} = 5\sqrt{2}$ *[1 mark]*
     [6 marks available in total — as above]

4   Face A: $P = \dfrac{F}{A}$, so $10 = \dfrac{120}{A}$, which means area of face A = 12 m²
     So $(x + 1) \times y = 12$ or $xy + y = 12$ [1]
     Face B: $P = \dfrac{F}{A}$, so $7.5 = \dfrac{120}{A}$, which means area of face B = 16 m²
     So $(x + 3) \times y = 16$ or $xy + 3y = 16$ [2]
     [2] – [1]: $2y = 4$, so $y = 2$
     $xy + y = 12$, so $2x + 2 = 12$, which means $2x = 10$ so $x = 5$
     Volume = $(5 + 1) \times (5 + 3) \times 2 = 6 \times 8 \times 2 = 96$ m³
     [6 marks available — 1 mark for finding the areas of faces A and
     B, 1 mark for finding an equation for the area of face A, 1 mark
     for finding an equation for the area of face B, 1 mark for solving
     the simultaneous equations to find the value of y, 1 mark for
     finding the value of x, 1 mark for the correct volume]
     There are other ways of doing one — you could start by finding
     expressions for the pressure exerted by each face in terms of x and y.

5    $2x - 5 = -x^2 + 15x - 41$ *[1 mark]*
     $x^2 - 13x + 36 = 0$
     $(x - 4)(x - 9) = 0$ *[1 mark]*, so $x = 4$ or $x = 9$ *[1 mark]*
     When $x = 4$, $y = 2(4) - 5 = 3$
     When $x = 9$, $y = 2(9) - 5 = 13$ *[1 mark for both y-values]*
     $ABDC$ is a trapezium with $CD = 9 - 4 = 5$, $AC = 3$ and $BD = 13$
     [1 mark for all lengths correct],
     so area = $\dfrac{1}{2}(3 + 13) \times 5 = 40$ units² *[1 mark]*
     [6 marks available in total — as above]

Answers

Page 23: Sequences

1   The first term, a, is $(5 \times 1) - 3 = 2$ and the common difference, d, is 5. *[1 mark]*
Using $a = 2$ and $d = 5$, the sum of the first 77 terms is
$\frac{77}{2}(2 \times 2 + (77 - 1) \times 5) = 14\,784$ *[1 mark]*
Look for n such that $5n - 3 > 14\,784$
$5n > 14\,787$ so $n > 2957.4$ *[1 mark]*
The smallest integer value of n is 2958 and the value of the 2958th term is $5 \times 2958 - 3 = 14\,787$ *[1 mark]*
[4 marks available in total — as above]

2   There were 18 entries in week 3 so $a + 2d = 18$ [1] *[1 mark]*
There were 288 entries in the first 9 weeks so
$\frac{9}{2}(2a + 8d) = 288$ [2] *[1 mark]*
From [1], $a = 18 - 2d$. Substituting that into [2] gives
$\frac{9}{2}(2(18 - 2d) + 8d) = 288$
$9(18 - 2d + 4d) = 288$
$162 + 18d = 288$ so $d = 7$ *[1 mark]*
Substituting $d = 7$ into [1] gives $a + (2 \times 7) = 18$ so $a = 4$ *[1 mark]*
In the 30th week there will be $4 + (29 \times 7) = 207$ entries *[1 mark]*
[5 marks available in total — as above]

3   Difference between the first and second terms:
$(8x - 29) - (6x + 1) = 2x - 30$
Difference between the second and third terms:
$(5x + 6) - (8x - 29) = -3x + 35$
In an arithmetic sequence, the difference between each pair of terms is the same, so $2x - 30 = -3x + 35$
$5x = 65$, which means $x = 13$.
So the first three terms are $6(13) + 1 = 79$, $8(13) - 29 = 75$ and $5(13) + 6 = 71$. The nth term of this sequence is $83 - 4n$, so the 20th term is $83 - 4(20) = 83 - 80 = 3$.
[6 marks available — 1 mark for finding the differences between both pairs of terms, 1 mark for setting these expressions equal to each other, 1 mark for solving to find the value of x, 1 mark for using the value of x to find the first three terms, 1 mark for finding an expression for the nth term, 1 mark for using this expression to find the 20th term]

Pages 24-25: Proof

1   LHS: $(2n + 1)^3 - 1 \equiv (4n^2 + 4n + 1)(2n + 1) - 1$
$\equiv 8n^3 + 4n^2 + 8n^2 + 4n + 2n + 1 - 1$
$\equiv 8n^3 + 12n^2 + 6n \equiv 2n(4n^2 + 6n + 3) \equiv$ RHS
[3 marks available — 1 mark for correctly expanding cubed bracket, 1 mark for simplifying, 1 mark for factorising to show that LHS ≡ RHS]

2   Take two consecutive numbers, n and $n + 1$.
Their squares are n^2 and $(n + 1)^2 = n^2 + 2n + 1$. *[1 mark]*
The difference between their squares is
$(n^2 + 2n + 1) - n^2 = 2n + 1$. *[1 mark]*
The sum of the numbers is $n + (n + 1) = 2n + 1$, which is the same as the difference of their squares. *[1 mark]*
[3 marks available in total — as above]

3   If a and b are both odd, then let $a = 2m + 1$ and $b = 2n + 1$ for integers m and n. Then $a + b = (2m + 1) + (2n + 1) = 2m + 2n + 2$
$= 2(m + n + 1) = 2x$ (where $x = m + n + 1$) *[1 mark]*. So $a + b$ is always even, which means that $(a + b)^{40} = (2x)^{40} = 2^{40}x^{40} = 2(2^{39}x^{40})$
$= 2y$, where $y = (2^{39}x^{40})$ *[1 mark]*, which is even.
[2 marks available in total — as above]

4   Take three consecutive numbers, n, $n + 1$ and $n + 2$.
Their cubes are n^3, $(n + 1)^3 = (n^2 + 2n + 1)(n + 1)$
$= n^3 + n^2 + 2n^2 + 2n + n + 1 = n^3 + 3n^2 + 3n + 1$
and $(n + 2)^3 = (n^2 + 4n + 4)(n + 2) = n^3 + 2n^2 + 4n^2 + 8n + 4n + 8$
$= n^3 + 6n^2 + 12n + 8$.
Their sum is $n^3 + n^3 + 3n^2 + 3n + 1 + n^3 + 6n^2 + 12n + 8$
$= 3n^3 + 9n^2 + 15n + 9 = 3(n^3 + 3n^2 + 5n + 3) = 3x$
(where $x = n^3 + 3n^2 + 5n + 3$).
Any integer multiplied by 3 is a multiple of 3, so the sum of any three consecutive cube numbers is a multiple of 3.
[4 marks available — 1 mark for the correct expansion of $(n + 1)^3$, 1 mark for the correct expansion of $(n + 2)^3$, 1 mark for adding the terms and simplifying the result, 1 mark for writing as a multiple of 3]

5   Max's number $= 5n + 1$ for some integer n
The square of Max's number is $(5n + 1)^2 = (5n + 1)(5n + 1)$
$= 25n^2 + 10n + 1$
Samira's number $= 5n - 3$ and the square of her number is
$(5n - 3)(5n - 3) = 25n^2 - 30n + 9$
Difference $= (25n^2 + 10n + 1) - (25n^2 - 30n + 9) = 40n - 8$
$= 8(5n - 1) = 8x$ (where $x = 5n - 1$)
Any integer multiplied by 8 is a multiple of 8, so the difference between the squares of their numbers is a multiple of 8.
[5 marks available — 1 mark for finding an expression for Max's number, 1 mark for finding an expression for Samira's number, 1 mark for squaring both numbers, 1 mark for finding the difference between the squares, 1 mark for writing as a multiple of 8]
Here, you could have written the difference as $(5n + 1)^2 - (5n - 3)^2$ and used the difference of two squares to find the expression $40n - 8$.

6   $3^8 - 7^4 = (3^4)^2 - (7^2)^2 = (3^4 + 7^2)(3^4 - 7^2)$
$= (81 + 49)(81 - 49) = 130 \times 32$
$= 13 \times 10 \times 32 = 13x$ (where $x = 10 \times 32$)
Any integer multiplied by 13 is a multiple of 13, so $3^8 - 7^4$ is a multiple of 13.
[3 marks available — 1 mark for factorising using the difference of two squares, 1 mark for finding the value of each factor, 1 mark for writing as a multiple of 13]

7   $15^{12} + 12^{16} = (3 \times 5)^{12} + (3 \times 2^2)^{16}$
$= (3^{12} \times 5^{12}) + (3^{16} \times 2^{32})$ *[1 mark]*
$= 3^2[(3^{10} \times 5^{12}) + (3^{14} \times 2^{32})]$ *[1 mark]*
$= 9[(3^{10} \times 5^{12}) + (3^{14} \times 2^{32})]$
$= 9x$ (where $x = (3^{10} \times 5^{12}) + (3^{14} \times 2^{32})$) *[1 mark]*
Any integer multiplied by 9 is a multiple of 9, so $15^{12} + 12^{16}$ is a multiple of 9.
[3 marks available in total — as above]

Pages 26-27: Direct and Inverse Proportion

1   a) $f \propto d$, so $f = kd$ *[1 mark]*
When $d = 84$, $f = 3$ so $3 = k \times 84$, so $k = \frac{3}{84} = \frac{1}{28}$ *[1 mark]*
So $f = \frac{d}{28}$ or $d = 28f$ *[1 mark]*
[3 marks available in total — as above]

   b)   Distance = Speed × Time
The motorbike travels $70 \times 5.4 = 378$ km *[1 mark]*
When $d = 378$ km, $f = \frac{378}{28} = 13.5$ litres *[1 mark]*
[2 marks available in total — as above]

2   a) $w \propto r^3$, so $w = kr^3$ *[1 mark]*
When $r = 6$, $w = 1080$, so $1080 = k \times 6^3$, so $k = 5$ *[1 mark]*
So $w = 5r^3$
When $w = 8640$, $5r^3 = 8640$ *[1 mark]*
$r^3 = 1728$, so $r = 12$ *[1 mark]*
[4 marks available in total — as above]

b)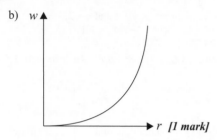

w ↑

→ r *[1 mark]*

3 $p \propto q$ and $q \propto \dfrac{1}{r}$ so $p = Aq$ and $q = \dfrac{B}{r}$ *[1 mark for both]*

When $p = 8$, $q = 25$ so $A = 8 \div 25 = 0.32$ *[1 mark]*

When $q = 25$, $r = 16$ so $B = 25 \times 16 = 400$ *[1 mark]*

So when $r = 2$, $q = \dfrac{400}{2} = 200$ *[1 mark]*

And so $p = 0.32 \times 200 = 64$ *[1 mark]*

[5 marks available in total — as above]

4 $a \propto \dfrac{1}{b}$ and $a \propto \dfrac{1}{c^2}$ so $a = \dfrac{M}{b}$ and $a = \dfrac{N}{c^2}$

Substituting for a gives: $\dfrac{M}{b} = \dfrac{N}{c^2}$ and so

$b = \dfrac{M}{N}c^2$ where $\dfrac{M}{N}$ is just a constant so $b \propto c^2$.

[3 marks available — 1 mark for writing both proportions as equations, 1 mark for substituting for a to equate the two fractions, 1 mark for rearranging into the form $b = kc^2$ where k is a constant and explaining that this is the equation of a direct proportion]

5 Let the object have density $= d_1$ and volume $= v$.
Call the object's density after the increase d_2.
Volume of the object after the increase $= 1.4v$.

$d \propto \dfrac{1}{v}$ so $d_1 = \dfrac{k}{v}$ and $d_2 = \dfrac{k}{1.4v}$ *[1 mark]*

k is the same in both cases as the mass of the object doesn't change.

$d_1 v = k$ and $1.4 d_2 v = k$

$d_1 v = 1.4 d_2 v$

$d_1 = 1.4 d_2$ *[1 mark]*

So $d_2 = \dfrac{1}{1.4} d_1 = 0.71428... d_1$ *[1 mark]*

d_2 is 71.428...% of d_1, so the percentage decrease is
$100 - 71.428... = 28.571... = 28.6\%$ (1 d.p.) *[1 mark]*

[4 marks available in total — as above]

6 $y \propto \dfrac{1}{x^2}$ and $y \propto z^3$ so $y = \dfrac{A}{x^2}$ and $y = Bz^3$ *[1 mark for both]*

From the graph, when $x = 3$, $y = 80$ so $A = 80 \times 3^2 = 720$ *[1 mark]*

So when $x = 2$, $y = \dfrac{720}{2^2} = 180$ *[1 mark]*

When $y = 180$, $z = 5$, so $B = 180 \div 5^3 = 1.44$ *[1 mark]*

So when $z = 15$, $y = 1.44 \times 15^3 = 4860$ *[1 mark]*

[5 marks available in total — as above]

Section 3 – Graphs, Functions and Calculus

Pages 28-29: Coordinates and Radio

1 a) Difference in x-coordinates from A to M: $4 - -2 = 6$
M is the midpoint of AB, so difference in x-coordinates from M to $B = 6$, so x-coordinate of $B = 4 + 6 = 10$ *[1 mark]*,
Difference in y-coordinates from A to M: $5 - 2 = 3$,
so difference in y-coordinates from M to $B = 3$,
so y-coordinate of $B = 5 + 3 = 8$ *[1 mark]*.
So the coordinates of B are (10, 8).
[2 marks available in total — as above]

b) Difference in x-coordinates from M to B: $10 - 4 = 6$
Difference in y-coordinates from M to B: $8 - 5 = 3$

P is $\dfrac{1}{3}$ of the way along MB,

so the x-coordinate of P is $4 + (\dfrac{1}{3} \times 6) = 6$

and the y-coordinate of P is $5 + (\dfrac{1}{3} \times 3) = 6$
So the coordinates of P are (6, 6).
Difference between x-coordinates of A and P: $6 - -2 = 8$
Difference between x-coordinates of A and B: $10 - -2 = 12$
so the ratio $AP:AB = 8:12 = 2:3$
[3 marks available — 1 mark for a correct method to find the coordinates of P, 1 mark for the correct coordinates of P, 1 mark for the correct ratio]
Instead of finding the coordinates of P, you could have found AP and AB in terms of MP and used this to find the ratio.

2 Coordinates of C are $(2 + 4, -1) = (6, -1)$
Coordinates of M are $(2 + 2, -1 + 2) = (4, 1)$
Difference in x-coordinates from E to M: $4 - 0 = 4$
Difference in x-coordinates from M to C: $6 - 4 = 2$
So $EM:MC = 4:2 = 2:1$
[3 marks available — 1 mark for finding the coordinates of C and M, 1 mark for finding the differences between the x- or y-coordinates of E & M and M & C, 1 mark for the correct ratio]

3 Difference in x-coordinates from E to B: $6 - 0 = 6$
Difference in y-coordinates from E to B: $4 - -4 = 8$

P is $\dfrac{3}{4}$ of the way along EB, so has x-coordinate $0 + \dfrac{3}{4} \times 6 = 4.5$

and y-coordinate $-4 + \dfrac{3}{4} \times 8 = 2$, so P has coordinates (4.5, 2).

$PF^2 = (6 - 4.5)^2 + (0 - 2)^2 = 6.25$, so $PF = \sqrt{6.25} = 2.5$.
[4 marks available — 1 mark for correct difference in x- and y-coordinates of E and B, 1 mark for correct coordinates of P, 1 mark for using Pythagoras to find PF^2, 1 mark for the correct answer]

4 Difference in x-coordinates from A to M: $3 - -2 = 5$
M is the midpoint of AC, so difference in x-coordinates from M to $C = 5$, so x-coordinate of $C = 3 + 5 = 8$
C has the same y-coordinate as D, so the coordinates of C are (8, 2)
Difference in x-coordinates from M to C: $8 - 3 = 5$
Difference in y-coordinates from M to C: $2 - 4.5 = -2.5$

N is $\dfrac{3}{5}$ of the way along MC,

so the x-coordinate of N is $3 + \dfrac{3}{5} \times 5 = 6$

and the y-coordinate of N is $4.5 + \dfrac{3}{5} \times -2.5 = 3$

So the coordinates of N are (6, 3).
B has the same y-coordinate as A, and the difference in x-coordinates of C and D is $8 - -5 = 13$, so the x-coordinate of B is $-2 + 13 = 11$. So B has coordinates (11, 7).
Distance $NB^2 = (11 - 6)^2 + (7 - 3)^2 = 5^2 + 4^2 = 41$
$NB = \sqrt{41}$
[6 marks available — 1 mark for the correct coordinates of C, 1 mark for a correct method to find the coordinates of N, 1 mark for correct coordinates of N, 1 mark for the correct coordinates of B, 1 mark for a correct method to find the distance NB, 1 mark for the correct answer]
There are different ways to find the coordinates of N and C.

Page 30: Gradients

1 a) Gradient of line connecting (10, 15) and (20, 20)
= average acceleration between 10 and 20 seconds
$$= \frac{20 - 15}{20 - 10} = \frac{5}{10} = 0.5 \text{ m/s}^2$$
[2 marks available — 2 marks for correct answer, otherwise 1 mark for correct coordinates of the two points]

b) Draw a tangent to the graph at 50 seconds, e.g.

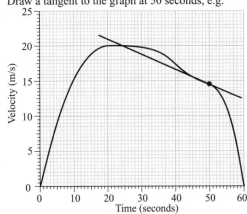

Gradient of tangent at 50 seconds = gradient of line connecting (29, 19) and (57, 13):
$$\frac{13 - 19}{57 - 29} = \frac{-6}{28} = -0.21428... = -0.214 \text{ m/s}^2 \text{ (3 s.f.)}$$
[2 marks available — 2 marks for the correct answer, otherwise 1 mark for correctly drawing the tangent]
It can be a bit tricky to draw the tangent exactly — as long as you got a similar answer, you'll be fine.

2 a) Draw a tangent to the graph at 35 mins, e.g.

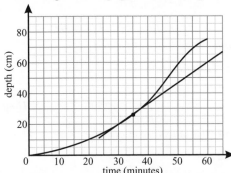

Gradient of tangent at 35 mins = gradient of line connecting (45, 40) and (60, 60): $\frac{60 - 40}{60 - 45} = \frac{20}{15} = \frac{4}{3}$ cm/min
[2 marks available — 2 marks for the correct answer, otherwise 1 mark for correctly drawing the tangent]

b) After 60 mins, the water is 75 cm deep, so average rate
= gradient of line connecting (0, 0) and (60, 75):
$$= \frac{75 - 0}{60 - 0} = \frac{75}{60} = 1.25 \text{ cm/min}$$
[2 marks available — 2 marks for the correct answer, otherwise 1 mark for correct coordinates of the two points]

Pages 31-32: Perpendicular Lines

1 Gradient of L_1: $\frac{20 - 6}{11 - 4} = \frac{14}{7} = 2$,

so gradient of line $L_2 = -1 \div 2 = -\frac{1}{2}$

L_2 passes through (28, 0), so $0 = -\frac{1}{2}(28) + c$
$0 = -14 + c$, so $c = 14$
So the equation of line L_2 is $y = -\frac{1}{2}x + 14$

[3 marks available — 1 mark for finding the gradient of line L_1, 1 mark for finding the gradient of L_2, 1 mark for the correct answer]

2 Gradient of $SQ = 4$
The diagonals of a kite cross at right angles so are perpendicular, so gradient of $PR = -\frac{1}{4}$.
Point R has coordinates (8, 15), so $15 = -\frac{1}{4}(8) + c$
$15 = -2 + c$, so $c = 17$
So the equation of PR is $y = -\frac{1}{4}x + 17$

[3 marks available — 1 mark for stating that the diagonals of a kite are perpendicular, 1 mark for finding the gradient of PR, 1 mark for the correct answer]

3 Equation of L_1 is $x + 5y = 100$, or $y = -\frac{1}{5}x + 20$, so has gradient $-\frac{1}{5}$.
L_2 is perpendicular to L_1 so has gradient $-1 \div -\frac{1}{5} = 5$.
L_2 passes through (2, 4), so $4 = 5(2) + c$
$4 = 10 + c$, so $c = -6$
So the equation of line L_2 is $y = 5x - 6$
At M, $-\frac{1}{5}x + 20 = 5x - 6$
$26 = \frac{26}{5}x$, so $x = 5$
When $x = 5$, $y = 5(5) - 6 = 25 - 6 = 19$
So the coordinates of M are (5, 19).
[5 marks available — 1 mark for finding the gradient of L_1, 1 mark for finding the gradient of L_2, 1 mark for finding the equation of L_2, 1 mark for setting the equations for L_1 and L_2 equal to each other and solving to find x or y, 1 mark for the correct answer]
Check your answer by putting your x-coordinate into the equation of L_1 and checking you get the correct y-coordinate.

4 Equation of L_1 is $2y - x = 14$, or $y = \frac{1}{2}x + 7$ so has gradient $\frac{1}{2}$
L_2 is perpendicular to L_1 so has gradient $-1 \div \frac{1}{2} = -2$.
L_2 passes through point (6, 10) so $10 = -2(6) + c$
$10 = -12 + c$, so $c = 22$. So the equation of L_2 is $y = -2x + 22$
R is the y-intercept of L_2, so the y-coordinate of R is 22.
RQ is horizontal so the y-coordinate of Q is 22

Q lies on L_1 so $22 = \frac{1}{2}x + 7$
$15 = \frac{1}{2}x$ so $x = 30$
So the coordinates of Q are (30, 22).
[5 marks available — 1 mark for finding the gradient of L_1, 1 mark for finding the gradient of L_2, 1 mark for finding the equation of L_2, 1 mark for finding the y-coordinate of Q, 1 mark for the correct answer]

5 Equation of L_1 is $2x + 3y = 12$, or $y = -\frac{2}{3}x + 4$, so has gradient $-\frac{2}{3}$.
L_2 is parallel to L_1, so also has gradient $-\frac{2}{3}$.
L_2 passes through (6, 13), so $13 = -\frac{2}{3}(6) + c_2$
$13 = -4 + c_2$, so $c_2 = 17$. So the equation of L_2 is $y = -\frac{2}{3}x + 17$.
L_3 is perpendicular to L_1 and L_2 so has gradient $\frac{3}{2}$.
It passes through (3, 2) so $2 = \frac{3}{2}(3) + c_3$
$2 = \frac{9}{2} + c_3$, so $c_3 = -\frac{5}{2}$. So the equation of L_3 is $y = \frac{3}{2}x - \frac{5}{2}$
When L_2 and L_3 intersect, $-\frac{2}{3}x + 17 = \frac{3}{2}x - \frac{5}{2}$
$\frac{39}{2} = \frac{13}{6}x$ so $x = 9$.
When $x = 9$, $y = -\frac{2}{3}(9) + 17 = -6 + 17 = 11$
So L_2 and L_3 intersect at (9, 11).
[6 marks available — 1 mark for finding the gradient of L_1, 1 mark for finding the equation of L_2, 1 mark for finding the gradient of L_3, 1 mark for finding the equation of L_3, 1 mark for setting the equations for L_2 and L_3 equal to each other and solving to find x or y, 1 mark for the correct answer]

Page 33-34: Harder Graphs

1   The two closest points are (3, 3) and (–3, –3).
    Use Pythagoras to find the distance between them, d:
    $d^2 = (3 - -3)^2 + (3 - -3)^2 = 6^2 + 6^2 = 72$, so $d = \sqrt{72} = 6\sqrt{2}$
    *[3 marks available — 1 mark for finding the two closest points,
    1 mark for using Pythagoras to find the distance, 1 mark for the
    correct answer]*

2   a)

x	y
–2	5.25
–1.5	4.9444...
–1	5
–0.5	7.5
–0.2	28.2
0.2	27.8
0.5	6.5
1	3
1.5	1.9444...
2	1.25

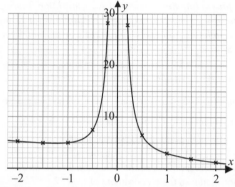

    *[3 marks available — 1 mark for a correct table, 1 mark for
    plotting the points correctly, 1 mark for smooth curves drawn
    through all the points]*

    b) $\frac{1}{x^2} - 6x - 9 = 0 \Rightarrow \frac{1}{x^2} - x + 3 = 5x + 12$ so draw the line of
         $y = 5x + 12$ on your diagram.

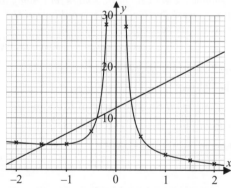

    The solutions are where the two lines intersect, so at
    $x = -1.4$ (1 d.p.), $x = -0.4$ (1 d.p.) and $x = 0.3$ (1 d.p.).
    *[3 marks available — 1 mark for rearranging the equation
    to find 5x + 12, 1 mark for drawing the line correctly,
    1 mark for the correct answers]*
    Allow solutions within ±0.1 of the values given.

    c)   From the graph, the maximum integer value of b where $y = b$
         only intersects $y = \frac{1}{x^2} - x + 3$ once is $b = 4$. So $4 = \frac{1}{x^2} - x + 3$
         $\Rightarrow \frac{1}{x^2} - x - 1 = 0$. Therefore the maximum value of a such
         where $y = \frac{1}{x^2} - x - a$ only has one solution is $a = 1$.

         *[2 marks available — 1 mark for saying y = 4 is the
         maximum horizontal line to only intersect once, 1 mark for
         a correct explanation for the value of a]*

3   Find the equation of the line that should be drawn:
    $x^2 + x = 1$
    $x^2 + x - 4 = -3$
    $x^2 - x - 4 = -3 - 2x$
    So draw the line $y = -3 - 2x$ to find the solutions *[1 mark]*:

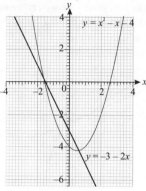

    [1 mark]
    So solutions to $x^2 + x = 1$ are $x \approx -1.6$ *[1 mark]* and $x \approx 0.6$ *[1 mark]*
    [4 marks available in total — as above]

4   Putting $A(-1, 5)$ into $y = ax^3 - bx + 2a$ gives
    $5 = -a + b + 2a \Rightarrow a + b = 5$ [1] *[1 mark]*
    Putting $B(2, 14)$ into $y = ax^3 - bx + 2a$ gives
    $14 = 8a - 2b + 2a \Rightarrow 10a - 2b = 14 \Rightarrow 5a - b = 7$ [2] *[1 mark]*
    Adding equations [1] and [2] gives $6a = 12 \Rightarrow a = 2$ *[1 mark]*
    Substituting $a = 2$ back into [1] gives $2 + b = 5 \Rightarrow b = 3$ *[1 mark]*
    So $y = 2ax^3 - 4ax - 2b$
    $\quad = (2 \times 2)x^3 - (4 \times 2)x - (2 \times 3) = 4x^3 - 8x - 6$ *[1 mark]*
    Putting $x = -1$ gives $y = -4 + 8 - 6 = -2$ so $C = (-1, -2)$
    Putting $x = 2$ gives $y = 32 - 16 - 6 = 10$ so $D = (2, 10)$.
    [1 mark for finding both C and D]
    Gradient of $CD = \frac{10 - (-2)}{2 - (-1)} = \frac{12}{3} = 4$ *[1 mark]*
    [7 marks available in total — as above]

Pages 35-36: Trig Graphs

1   $x = 285°$ *[1 mark]*

2   Using the symmetry of the graph, $x = 90° - 15° = 75°$ *[1 mark]*
    and $x = 270° - 15° = 255°$ *[1 mark]*
    [2 marks available in total — as above]

3   $\frac{6 + \sqrt{2}}{2} = \sin 2x + 3$

    $\Rightarrow 0.7071... = \sin 2x$ *[1 mark]*
    $\Rightarrow 2x = \sin^{-1}(0.7071...)$
    $\Rightarrow 2x = 45° \Rightarrow x = 22.5°$ *[1 mark]*
    [2 marks available in total — as above]
    *You didn't actually need the graph for this one — it's just there to give
    you an idea of the shape.*

4   a)   Using the symmetry of the graph,
         $x = 180° - 55° = 125°$ *[1 mark]*

    b)   Extending the graph, $x = 180° + 55° = 235°$ *[1 mark]*

    c)   The cos graph has a line of symmetry at $x = 0$,
         so $x = -55°$ *[1 mark]*

5   The two graphs intersect when $x = 45°$, so $\tan 45° = -\sin 45° + c$,
    which means $c = \tan 45° + \sin 45°$ *[1 mark]*

    so $c = 1 + \frac{1}{\sqrt{2}}$ *[1 mark]*
    At $(90°, a)$,

    $a = -\sin 90° + 1 + \frac{1}{\sqrt{2}} = \frac{1}{\sqrt{2}} = 0.7071... = 0.71$ (2 d.p.) *[1 mark]*
    [3 marks available in total — as above]

Pages 37-38: Functions

1 a) fg(4) = f(g(4)) = f(4² + 4) = f(20) = $\sqrt{2(20)-8}$ = $\sqrt{32}$ = $4\sqrt{2}$
[2 marks available — 1 mark for finding the value of g(4), 1 mark for using this value to find fg(4), giving the answer as a simplified surd]
You could have found an expression for fg(x) and put in x = 4.

b) gf(x) = g(f(x)) = g($\sqrt{2x-8}$) = ($\sqrt{2x-8}$)² + 4 *[1 mark]*
= 2x − 8 + 4 = 2x − 4 *[1 mark]*
[2 marks available in total — as above]

c) Write out x = f(y): x = $\sqrt{2y-8}$ *[1 mark]*
Rearrange to make y the subject: x² = 2y − 8 *[1 mark]*
x² + 8 = 2y
y = $\frac{x^2+8}{2}$, so f⁻¹(x) = $\frac{x^2+8}{2}$ *[1 mark]*
[3 marks available in total — as above]

2 a) fg(x) = f(g(x)) = f(sin x) = 2 sin x − 1 *[1 mark]*
2 sin x − 1 = 0
2 sin x = 1
sin x = $\frac{1}{2}$ *[1 mark]*
So x = 30° *[1 mark]* and x = 180° − 30° = 150° *[1 mark]*
[4 marks available in total — as above]

b) gf(x) = sin(2x − 1) so gf(x) has the same range as sin x, i.e. −1 ≤ gf(x) ≤ 1 *[1 mark]*

3 Write out x = f(y): x = $\frac{y+5}{2}$ *[1 mark]*
Rearrange to make y the subject: 2x = y + 5
y = 2x − 5, so f⁻¹(x) = 2x − 5 *[1 mark]*
Write out x = g(y): x = 3y − 10 *[1 mark]*
Rearrange to make y the subject: x + 10 = 3y
y = $\frac{x+10}{3}$, so g⁻¹(x) = $\frac{x+10}{3}$ *[1 mark]*
When f⁻¹(x) = g⁻¹(x), 2x − 5 = $\frac{x+10}{3}$ *[1 mark]*
6x − 15 = x + 10
5x = 25 so x = 5 *[1 mark]*
[6 marks available in total — as above]

4 a) fgg(x) = f(g(g(x))) = f(g(x + 2))
= f((x + 2) + 2) = f(x + 4) *[1 mark]*
= (x + 4)² + 4(x + 4) + 3 *[1 mark]*
= x² + 8x + 16 + 4x + 16 + 3
= x² + 12x + 35 *[1 mark]*
[3 marks available in total — as above]

b) fgg(x) = 0 means that x² + 12x + 35 = 0
(x + 7)(x + 5) = 0, so x = −7 or x = −5
[2 marks available — 1 mark for setting expression from part a) equal to 0 and factorising, 1 mark for both correct x-values]

5 a) fg(x) = f(g(x)) = f(2x + 1) = $\frac{4(2x+1)}{(2x+1)+9}$ = $\frac{8x+4}{2x+10}$
= $\frac{4x+2}{x+5}$ *[1 mark]*
So $\frac{4x+2}{x+5}$ = x *[1 mark]*
4x + 2 = x(x + 5)
4x + 2 = x² + 5x *[1 mark]*
0 = x² + x − 2 = (x + 2)(x − 1) *[1 mark]*
So x = −2 or x = 1 *[1 mark for both]*
[5 marks available in total — as above]

b) fg(x) = $\frac{4x+2}{x+5}$ is undefined when the denominator is 0
so x ≠ −5 *[1 mark]*

Pages 39-40: Graph Transformations

1 a)
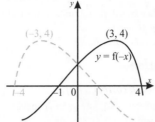

[3 marks available — 1 mark for reflecting the graph in the y-axis, 1 mark for the correct turning point, 1 mark for both correct x-intercepts]

b) Turning point = (−3 − 3, 4 + 2) = (−6, 6)
[2 marks available — 1 mark for the correct x-coordinate, 1 mark for the correct y-coordinate]

2 a)
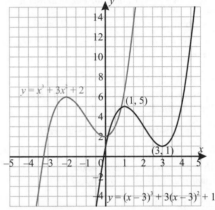

[3 marks available — 1 mark for a translation of 3 units to the right, 1 mark for a translation of 1 unit down, 1 mark for both correct turning points]

b) (x − 3)³ = (x − 3)(x − 3)(x − 3) = (x² − 6x + 9)(x − 3) *[1 mark]*
= x³ − 3x² − 6x² + 18x + 9x − 27
= x³ − 9x² + 27x − 27 *[1 mark]*
(x − 3)³ + 3(x − 3)² + 1
= x³ − 9x² + 27x − 27 + 3(x² − 6x + 9) + 1 *[1 mark]*
= x³ − 6x² + 9x + 1 *[1 mark]*
[4 marks available in total — as above]

3 a) 5 ÷ 2 = $\frac{5}{2}$, so the brackets are (x − $\frac{5}{2}$)² *[1 mark]*.
Expanding the brackets: (x − $\frac{5}{2}$)² = x² − 5x + $\frac{25}{4}$
To complete the square: 7 − $\frac{25}{4}$ = $\frac{3}{4}$ *[1 mark]*
So x² + 5x + 7 = (x − $\frac{5}{2}$)² + $\frac{3}{4}$.
So the coordinates of the turning point are ($\frac{5}{2}$, $\frac{3}{4}$) *[1 mark]*
[3 marks available in total — as above]
You could also set the derivative equal to zero and solve for x.

b) Turning point = ($\frac{5}{2}$ − 3, $\frac{3}{4}$ − 2) = (−$\frac{1}{2}$, −$\frac{5}{4}$)
[2 marks available — 1 mark for each correct coordinate]

c) x-intercepts are where f(x + 3) − 2 = 0
f(x + 3) − 2 = (x + 3)² − 5(x + 3) + 7 − 2 = x² + x − 1 *[1 mark]*
So x² + x − 1 = 0
x = $\frac{-1 \pm \sqrt{1^2 - (4 \times 1 \times -1)}}{2 \times 1}$ *[1 mark]* = $\frac{-1 \pm \sqrt{5}}{2}$
So x = $\frac{-1 + \sqrt{5}}{2}$ or x = $\frac{-1 - \sqrt{5}}{2}$ *[1 mark for both solutions]*
[3 marks available in total — as above]
You could use the completed square form to solve the equation.

4 a) $\frac{ab}{x-a}$ + b = $\frac{ab}{x-a}$ + $\frac{b(x-a)}{x-a}$ *[1 mark]*
= $\frac{ab + b(x-a)}{x-a}$ = $\frac{ab + bx - ab}{x-a}$ = $\frac{bx}{x-a}$ *[1 mark]*
[2 marks available in total — as above]

84

b) From part a), $\frac{3x}{x-2} = \frac{3(2)}{x-2} + 3 = \frac{6}{x-2} + 3$ *[1 mark]*
So the transformation is a translation 2 units to the right
[1 mark] and 3 units up *[1 mark]*.
[3 marks available in total — as above]

Pages 41-42: Differentiation

1 $\frac{dy}{dx} = 10x + 15$ *[1 mark for each correct term]*
So at $x = 4$ the gradient is $a = (10 \times 4) + 15 = 55$ *[1 mark]*
The gradient is $-a = -55$ when
$-55 = 10x + 15 \Rightarrow 10x = -70 \Rightarrow x = -7$ *[1 mark]*
When $x = -7$, $y = 5 \times (-7)^2 + (15 \times -7) + 3 = 143$
so the coordinates are $(-7, 143)$ *[1 mark]*
[5 marks available in total — as above]

2 $y = 4x - \frac{5}{x^2} \Rightarrow y = 4x - 5x^{-2}$
So $\frac{dy}{dx} = 4 + 10x^{-3} = 4 + \frac{10}{x^3}$ *[1 mark for each correct term]*
Turning point is when $\frac{dy}{dx} = 0$ so $0 = 4 + \frac{10}{x^3}$ *[1 mark]*
$\Rightarrow -4 = \frac{10}{x^3} \Rightarrow -4x^3 = 10 \Rightarrow x^3 = -2.5 \Rightarrow x = -1.3572...$ *[1 mark]*
When $x = -1.3572...$,
$y = (4 \times -1.3572...) - \frac{5}{(-1.3572...)^2} = -8.143...$
so the coordinates are $(-1.36, -8.14)$ (to 2 d.p.) *[1 mark]*
[5 marks available in total — as above]

3 a) $\frac{dy}{dx} = 3x^2 + 2bx$ *[1 mark for each correct term]*
At $x = -2$, $\frac{dy}{dx} = 0$ so $3 \times (-2)^2 + 2b \times (-2) = 0$ *[1 mark]*
$\Rightarrow 12 - 4b = 0 \Rightarrow b = \frac{12}{4} = 3$ *[1 mark]*
[4 marks available in total — as above]

  b) (i) $\frac{dy}{dx} = 3x^2 + (2 \times 3)x = 3x^2 + 6x$
The turning points are when $3x^2 + 6x = 0 \Rightarrow x(x + 2) = 0$
So the other turning point is at $x = 0$ *[1 mark]*
Substitute $x = 0$ into $y = x^3 + 3x^2 - 2$ to get
$y = 0^3 + 3 \times 0^2 - 2 = -2$
So the turning point is at $(0, -2)$ *[1 mark]*
[2 marks available in total — as above]

   (ii) The turning point is a minimum. The cubic has 2 turning points and the x^3 term is positive, so the shape of the graph means the first one at $x = -2$ must be a maximum and the turning point at $x = 0$ must be a minimum.
[2 marks available — 1 mark for the correct answer, 1 mark for an explanation referencing the general shape of a cubic with a positive x^3 coefficient]

4 $\frac{dh}{dt} = -6t^2 + 22t - 16$ *[1 mark for each correct term]*
$\frac{dh}{dt}$ is the velocity of the object, so find t when $\frac{dh}{dt} = 4$ m/s
$4 = -6t^2 + 22t - 16$ *[1 mark]*
$6t^2 - 22t + 20 = 0$
$3t^2 - 11t + 10 = 0$
$(3t - 5)(t - 2) = 0$ *[1 mark]* so $t = \frac{5}{3}$ and $t = 2$
The object will first be moving away from the ground at 4 m/s after $\frac{5}{3}$ seconds. *[1 mark]*
[6 marks available in total — as above]

5 a) The vertical height and base length have to be positive so:
$6 - 2x > 0 \Rightarrow x < 3$ and $4x + 1 > 0 \Rightarrow x > -0.25$
The possible values of x are $-0.25 < x < 3$.
[2 marks available — 1 mark for either $x < 3$ or $x > -0.25$, 1 mark for the correct answer]

  b) Area $= \frac{1}{2}(4x + 1)(6 - 2x) = \frac{1}{2}(-8x^2 + 22x + 6)$
$= -4x^2 + 11x + 3$ *[1 mark]*
Because the coefficient of x^2 is negative, the turning point is a maximum, so differentiate the expression and set equal to zero.
$-8x + 11 = 0$ *[1 mark for each correct term]*
So $x = \frac{11}{8} = 1.375$ *[1 mark]*
So maximum area $= -4(1.375^2) + (11 \times 1.375) + 3$
$= 10.5625$ km^2 *[1 mark]*
[5 marks available in total — as above]

6 If s is displacement then velocity $= v = \frac{ds}{dt}$
Taking the derivative of $s = -t^2 - \frac{4}{t} + 20$ gives
$v = \frac{ds}{dt} = -2t + \frac{4}{t^2}$ *[1 mark for each correct term]*
If v is velocity then acceleration $= a = \frac{dv}{dt}$
Taking the derivative of $v = -2t + \frac{4}{t^2}$ gives
$a = \frac{dv}{dt} = -2 - \frac{8}{t^3}$ *[1 mark for each correct term]*
If deceleration is 3 m/s then $-3 = -2 - \frac{8}{x^3}$ *[1 mark]*
So $-t^3 = -8$ and $t = 2$ seconds *[1 mark]*
[6 marks available in total — as above]

Section 4 – Geometry and Measures

Pages 43-45: Circle Geometry

1 E.g. By the alternate segment theorem, angle $ABC = x$ *[1 mark]*
As $AB = AC$, angle $ACB = x$ (isosceles triangle) *[1 mark]*
AB is parallel to DE, so angle $BAC = x$ (alternate angles) *[1 mark]*
All three angles inside the triangle are equal,
so ABC is an equilateral triangle. *[1 mark]*
[4 marks available in total — as above]
There's often more than one way to answer circle theorem questions — as long as you show clearly what you're doing, you'll get the marks.

2 E.g. Triangle AOD is isosceles,
so angle $ODA = (180° - 128°) \div 2 = 26°$ *[1 mark]*
Triangle BOC is also isosceles, so angle $OBC = 41°$ *[1 mark]*
$ABCD$ is a cyclic quadrilateral, so angle ABC + angle $CDA = 180°$
Angle $CDA = 180° - (59° + 41°) = 80°$ *[1 mark]*
Angle CDO = angle CDA – angle $ODA = 80° - 26° = 54°$ *[1 mark]*
[4 marks available in total — as above]

3 Triangle ABM is an equilateral triangle so $AM = AB = BM = 8$ cm.
$MB \times MD = ME \times MC$ (internal chord intersection rule)
So $8 \times 3 = ME \times 4$ *[1 mark]*, therefore $ME = 6$ cm *[1 mark]*
$FC \times FE = FB \times FA$ (external chord intersection rule)
$(14 + 6 + 4) \times 14 = (FA + 8) \times FA$ *[1 mark]*
$336 = FA^2 + 8FA$ so $FA^2 + 8FA - 336 = 0$ *[1 mark]*
Using the quadratic formula:
$FA = \frac{-8 \pm \sqrt{8^2 - (4 \times 1 \times -336)}}{2}$ *[1 mark]*
$= -22.7616...$ and $14.7616...$
So $FA = 14.8$ cm (3 s.f.) as length must be positive. *[1 mark]*
[6 marks available in total — as above]
You could also use the sine rule once you've found the length of ME.

4 E.g. Angle $CDE = 44°$ (the angle at the centre is double the angle at the circumference) *[1 mark]*
Angle $FBC = 76°$ (angles in the same segment are equal) *[1 mark]*
Angle $BFE = 180° - 44° - 76° = 60°$ (angles in a triangle add up to $180°$, and BDF is a triangle) *[1 mark]*.
[3 marks available in total — as above]

5 E.g. By the alternate segment theorem, angle $DBC = 54°$ *[1 mark]*
DB is a straight line, so angle $DXC = 180° - 94° = 86°$ *[1 mark]*
If X was the centre of the circle, then angle $DXC = 2 \times$ angle DBC *[1 mark]*. But $2 \times$ angle $DBC = 2 \times 54° = 108° \neq 86°$ *[1 mark]*,
so X is not the centre of the circle.
[4 marks available in total — as above]

6 E.g. Angle AFB = angle ABF (tangents from the same point are the same length, so triangle ABF is isosceles)
Angle AFB = angle ABF = $(180° - 36°) \div 2 = 72°$ *[1 mark]*
Angle AFO = $90°$ (tangent meets a radius at $90°$),
so angle BFO = angle FBO = $90° - 72° = 18°$ *[1 mark]*
Angle FEC = $180° - 56° - 18° = 106°$ *[1 mark]*
(opposite angles in a cyclic quadrilateral add up to $180°$)
Angle DCE = $180° - 112° = 68°$ and angle DEC = $180° - 106°$
= $74°$ *[1 mark for DCE and DEC]* (angles on a straight line)
Angle CDE = $180° - 68° - 74° = 38°$ *[1 mark]*
[5 marks available in total — as above]

7 E.g. Angle ACB = $x°$ (by the alternate segment theorem) *[1 mark]*
Angle OCF = $90°$ (tangent meets a radius at $90°$) *[1 mark]*
So angle OCA = $90 - y°$ *[1 mark]*
a = angle ACB – angle OCA = $x - (90° - y) = x + y - 90°$ *[1 mark]*
[4 marks available in total — as above]

Pages 46-48: Enlargement

1 a) Ratio of surface areas = $1^2 : 3^2 : 5^2 = 1 : 9 : 25$ *[1 mark]*
 b) Height of large cylinder = $6 \times 5 = 30$ cm
   Find the radius of the large cylinder: $6750\pi = \pi \times r^2 \times 30$
   So $r^2 = 6750 \div 30 = 225$, which means $r = 15$ cm
   Radius of small cylinder = $15 \div 5 = 3$ cm,
   so radius of middle cylinder = $3 \times 3 = 9$ cm
   [3 marks available — 1 mark for finding the radius of the large cylinder, 1 mark for finding the radius of the small cylinder, 1 mark for the correct answer]

2 a) (Scale factor)^3 = $\dfrac{160}{2.5 \times 10^6}$ *[1 mark]* = $\dfrac{1}{15\,625}$,
   so scale factor = $\dfrac{1}{25}$ *[1 mark]*
   [2 marks available in total — as above]
 b) Surface area of original = $200 \times 25^2 = 125\,000 = 1.25 \times 10^5$ m^2
   [2 marks available — 1 mark for correct working, 1 mark for the correct answer in standard form]

3 a) Scale factor = $\sqrt[3]{\dfrac{768\pi}{324\pi}} = \sqrt[3]{\dfrac{64}{27}} = \dfrac{4}{3}$ *[1 mark]*
   Surface area of cone B = $216\pi \times \left(\dfrac{4}{3}\right)^2 = 384\pi$ cm^2 *[1 mark]*
   [2 marks available in total — as above]
 b) $3 : 4$ *[1 mark]*

4 a) Volume of cuboid A = $1.5 \times 2.5 \times 5 = 18.75$ cm^3
   Volume of cuboid B = $18.75 \times \left(\dfrac{8}{5}\right)^3 = 76.8$ cm^3
   [2 marks available — 1 mark for a correct method, 1 mark for the correct answer]
   You could have worked out the side lengths of cuboid B and multiplied them together to find the volume.
 b) Density = mass ÷ volume and 0.06 kg = 60 g
   Cuboid A: density = $60 \div 18.75 = 3.2$ g/cm^3
   Cuboid B: density = $60 \div 76.8 = 0.78125$ g/cm^3
   % decrease = $\dfrac{3.2 - 0.78125}{3.2} \times 100 = 75.585... = 75.6\%$ (3 s.f.)
   [3 marks available — 1 mark for finding the density of cuboid A, 1 mark for finding the density of cuboid B, 1 mark for the correct answer]

5 Height: scale factor from small vase to medium vase
= $\sqrt{\dfrac{160}{90}} = \sqrt{\dfrac{16}{9}} = \dfrac{4}{3}$ *[1 mark]*
So height of small vase = $20 \div \dfrac{4}{3} = 15$ cm *[1 mark]*
Volume: scale factor from small vase to large vase
= $\sqrt{\dfrac{1440}{90}} = \sqrt{16} = 4$ *[1 mark]*
Volume of large vase = 0.016 m^3 = $16\,000$ cm^3
So volume of small vase = $16\,000 \div 4^3 = 250$ cm^3 *[1 mark]*
[4 marks available in total — as above]

6 Scale factor = $\sqrt[3]{8.1 \div 2.4} = \sqrt[3]{3.375} = 1.5$ *[1 mark]*
Time taken to decorate large bead = $8 \times 1.5^2 = 18$ mins *[1 mark]*
Time taken to decorate 5 small beads and 4 large beads
= $(5 \times 8) + (4 \times 18) = 112$ mins *[1 mark]*
$1\dfrac{3}{4}$ hours = 105 mins so Anna does not have enough time to decorate all the beads *[1 mark]*.
[4 marks available in total — as above]

Pages 49-50: Arcs, Sectors and Segments

1 Area = $\dfrac{x}{360} \times 12^2 \times \pi$
$88\pi = \dfrac{144\pi x}{360} = \dfrac{2\pi x}{5}$
$x = 88 \times \dfrac{5}{2} = 220°$
[3 marks available — 1 mark for a correct formula for the area of a sector, 1 mark for substituting in the numbers correctly, 1 mark for the correct value of x]

2 a) Area of sector = $\dfrac{70}{360} \times 6^2 \times \pi = 7\pi$ cm^2
   Area of triangle = $\frac{1}{2} \times 6^2 \times \sin 70° = 16.914...$ cm^2
   Area of segment = $7\pi - 16.914... = 5.076... = 5.08$ cm^2 (3 s.f.)
   [3 marks available — 1 mark for finding the area of the sector, 1 mark for finding the area of the triangle, 1 mark for the correct answer]
 b) Perimeter of segment = arc + chord
   Arc length = $\dfrac{70}{360} \times 2 \times \pi \times 6 = \dfrac{7}{3}\pi$ cm
   To find the chord length, use the cosine rule:
   $a^2 = 6^2 + 6^2 - (2 \times 6 \times 6 \times \cos 70°) = 47.374...$
   $a = 6.882...$ cm
   Perimeter = $\dfrac{7}{3}\pi + 6.882... = 14.213... = 14.2$ cm (3 s.f.)
   [4 marks available — 1 mark for the arc length, 1 mark for putting the numbers into the cosine rule formula correctly, 1 mark for the chord length, 1 mark for the correct answer]

3 Arc length = $21.6 - 8 - 8 = 5.6$ cm *[1 mark]*
Circumference = $2 \times 8 \times \pi = 50.265...$ cm *[1 mark]*
$50.265... \div 5.6 = 8.975... \approx 9$ sectors in total *[1 mark]*
[3 marks available in total — as above]
Don't forget to round your answer — there'll be a whole number of sectors (and the original perimeter was rounded as well).

4 a) Area of segment with radius 8 cm = $(\dfrac{45}{360} \times 8^2 \times \pi)$
   $= 8\pi$ cm^2 *[1 mark]*
   Area of segment with radius 5 cm = $(\dfrac{45}{360} \times 5^2 \times \pi)$
   $= \dfrac{25}{8}\pi$ cm^2 *[1 mark]*
   Area of white icing = $8\pi - \dfrac{25}{8}\pi = 15.315...$
   $= 15.3$ cm^2 (3 s.f.) *[1 mark]*
   [3 marks available in total — as above]
   It's always a good idea to leave your working in terms of π for as long as possible — it means you don't lose any accuracy later on.
 b) Area of top of slice = $\dfrac{45}{360} \times 10^2 \times \pi = 12.5\pi$ cm^2 *[1 mark]*
   Volume of slice = $12.5\pi \times 8 = 100\pi = 314.159...$
   $= 314$ cm^3 (3 s.f.) *[1 mark]*
   [2 marks available in total — as above]

5 a) Angle DFC = $(360° - 140°) \div 2 = 110°$
   and angle DCF = $60° \div 2 = 30°$ *[1 mark for both]*
   Using the sine rule, $\dfrac{DC}{\sin 110°} = \dfrac{1.6}{\sin 30°}$ *[1 mark]*
   So $DC = \sin 110° \times \dfrac{1.6}{\sin 30°} = 3.0070...$
   $= 3.01$ cm (3 s.f.) *[1 mark]*
   [3 marks available in total — as above]
   There are other ways of answering this question — but you should still find that DC = 3.01 cm to 3 s.f.

b) From a), AD = 3.007... cm and AC = 6.014... cm
(as D is the midpoint of AC).
The diagram has a vertical line of symmetry, so $BE = AD$.
Arc length $AB = \frac{60}{360} \times 2 \times \pi \times 6.014...$ = 6.297... cm
Arc length $DE = \frac{140}{360} \times 2 \times \pi \times 1.6$ = 3.909... cm
Perimeter = 3.007... + 3.007... + 6.297... + 3.909...
= 16.221... = 16.2 cm (3 s.f.)
[5 marks available — 1 mark for finding AC, 1 mark for the correct lengths of AD and BE, 1 mark for the correct arc length AB, 1 mark for the correct arc length DE, 1 mark for the correct answer]

Pages 51-53: 3D Shapes — Surface Area and Volume

1 Area of cross-section = $\frac{1}{2}ab \sin C = \frac{1}{2} \times 4 \times 2 \times \sin 67°$
= 3.682... cm²
Volume of prism = 3.682... × 9 = 33.138... = 33.1 cm³ (3 s.f.)
[3 marks available — 1 mark for putting the numbers into the area formula correctly, 1 mark for the correct cross-sectional area, 1 mark for the correct answer]

2 Volume = $\frac{1}{3}\pi r^2 h$, so $(3.2 \times 10^{26})\pi = \frac{1}{3} \times \pi \times (4 \times 10^8)^2 \times x$
$(3.2 \times 10^{26})\pi = \frac{1}{3} \times \pi \times 16 \times 10^{16} \times x$
$9.6 \times 10^{26} = (1.6 \times 10^{17})x$
$\frac{9.6}{1.6} \times \frac{10^{26}}{10^{17}} = x$, so $x = 6 \times 10^9$ m
[3 marks available — 1 mark for squaring (4 × 10⁸) correctly, 1 mark for a correct method for solving the equation, 1 mark for the correct answer]

3 Let V_A = volume of sphere A, V_B = volume of sphere B and R_B = radius of sphere B. Then
$V_A = \frac{4}{3} \times \pi \times 6^3 = 288\pi$ cm³ *[1 mark]*
$V_B = 1.6 \times V_A = 1.6 \times 288\pi = 460.8\pi$ cm³ *[1 mark]*
$R_B^3 = 460.8\pi \div \frac{4}{3} \div \pi = 345.6$ *[1 mark]*
So $R_B = \sqrt[3]{345.6} = 7.017... = 7.02$ cm (3 s.f.) *[1 mark]*
[4 marks available in total — as above]

4 a) The removed cone is similar and is one-third of the height of the original cone, so has radius 5 cm and height 12 cm *[1 mark]*
Volume of new shape
$= (\frac{1}{3} \times \pi \times 15^2 \times 36) - (\frac{1}{3} \times \pi \times 5^2 \times 12)$ *[1 mark]*
$= 2700\pi - 100\pi = 2600\pi$ cm³ *[1 mark]*
[3 marks available in total — as above]

b) Use Pythagoras to find the slant height, l, of the original cone:
$l^2 = 36^2 + 15^2 = 1521$, so $l = \sqrt{1521} = 39$ cm *[1 mark]*
Slant height of removed cone = 39 ÷ 3 = 13 cm.
Surface area of new shape = curved area of original cone
– curved area of removed cone
+ both circular faces
$= (\pi \times 15 \times 39) - (\pi \times 5 \times 13) + (\pi \times 15^2) + (\pi \times 5^2)$ *[1 mark]*
$= 585\pi - 65\pi + 225\pi + 25\pi = 770\pi$ cm² *[1 mark]*
[3 marks available in total — as above]

5 Volume of cylinder = $\pi \times 10^2 \times 21 = 2100\pi$ cm³ *[1 mark]*
Volume of cone = $\frac{1}{3} \times \pi \times 10^2 \times 21 = 700\pi$ cm³ *[1 mark]*
Volume not taken up by the cone = $2100\pi - 700\pi$
$= 1400\pi$ cm³ *[1 mark]* = 0.0014π m³ *[1 mark]*
Density = mass ÷ volume, so mass = density × volume
mass = 0.52 × 0.0014π = 0.002287... kg *[1 mark]*
= 2.287... g = 2.29 g (3 s.f.) *[1 mark]*
[6 marks available in total — as above]
Be careful with the units here — you're given the dimensions of the shape in cm, but the density in kg/m³. It doesn't matter when you do the unit conversions, as long as you end up with an answer in g.

6 Cross-sectional area = $\frac{1}{2}ab \sin C$
$= \frac{1}{2} \times 2\sqrt{3} \times 4 \times \sin 60°$ *[1 mark]*
= 6 m² *[1 mark]*
Rate of flow = 90 000 litres per minute
= 90 000 ÷ 60 = 1500 litres per second *[1 mark]*
= 1 500 000 cm³/s = 1.5 m³/s *[1 mark]*
Speed = 1.5 ÷ 6 = 0.25 m/s *[1 mark]*
[5 marks available in total — as above]

7 Weight of one piece = 5000 ÷ 8 = 625 N *[1 mark]*
Area of flat face = $\pi r^2 \div 4 = \pi \times 1.4^2 \div 4 = 0.49\pi$ m² *[1 mark]*
Pressure = force ÷ area = 625 ÷ 0.49π *[1 mark]* = 406.007...
= 406 N/m² (3 s.f.) *[1 mark]*
[4 marks available in total — as above]

8 The slant length, l, of the cone is:
$\sqrt{(3k)^2 + (4k)^2} = \sqrt{9k^2 + 16k^2} = \sqrt{25k^2} = 5k$ cm *[1 mark]*
Curved surface area of cone = $\pi \times 3k \times 5k = 15k^2\pi$ *[1 mark]*
Curved surface area of hemisphere = $0.5 \times 4\pi(3k)^2 = 18k^2\pi$ *[1 mark]*
The total surface area of the object is
$15k^2\pi + 18k^2\pi = 33k^2\pi$ *[1 mark]*
So $33k^2\pi = 3993\pi$ *[1 mark]*, so $k^2 = 121$, so $k = 11$ *[1 mark]*
[6 marks available in total — as above]

9 Volume of one sphere = (30% of 1200) ÷ 2 = 180 cm³
$\frac{4}{3}\pi r^3 = 180$ *[1 mark]* so $r^3 = 42.971...$, so $r = 3.502...$ cm *[1 mark]*
Volume of one cone = (1200 ÷ 3) ÷ 4 = 100 cm³, so $\frac{1}{3}\pi r^2 h = 100$
$r = 3.502...$ cm, so $\frac{1}{3}\pi(3.502...)^2 h = 100$ *[1 mark]*
$h = 7.783...$ cm *[1 mark]*
Volume of cube = $(7.783...)^3 = 471.570...$ cm³ *[1 mark]*
Amount of steel left = 1200 – 360 – 400 = 440 cm³
so she does not have enough steel left *[1 mark]*
[6 marks available in total — as above]

Section Five – Pythagoras and Trigonometry

Pages 54-55: Trigonometry

1 The large rhombus has the following dimensions:
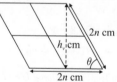
$h_v = 2n \times \sin\theta = 2n\sin\theta$ cm
Area of rhombus = $2n \times 2n\sin\theta = 4n^2\sin\theta$ cm²
[3 marks available — 1 mark for a correct method to work out the height of the large or small rhombus, 1 mark for the correct height, 1 mark for multiplying height by base length to get 4n²sin θ cm²]
You could also work out the area of one small rhombus then multiply it by 4 to get the area of the large rhombus.

2 Diagonals of a kite meet at right angles. So BOC = 90°.
$BO = \frac{10}{\tan 65°} = 4.663...$ cm *[1 mark]*
Angle $BAO = \tan^{-1}\left(\frac{4.663...}{4}\right) = 49.376...°$ *[1 mark]*
Angle DAO = angle BAO = 49.376...°
So angle BAD = 49.376...° + 49.376...° = 98.753...°
= 98.8° (1 d.p.) *[1 mark]*
[3 marks available in total — as above]

3 $AC = \sin 60° \times 4 = 3.464...$ km
$BD = \tan 55° \times 2 = 2.856...$ km *[1 mark for AC or BD]*
So the difference in height between A and B is
$3.464... - 2.856... = 0.607...$ km *[1 mark]*
$OC = \cos 60° \times 4 = 2$ km
So horizontal distance between A and B is $2 + 2 = 4$ km *[1 mark]*
Angle of depression $= \tan^{-1}\left(\dfrac{0.607...}{4}\right) = 8.640...°$
$= 8.6°$ (1 d.p.) *[1 mark]*
[4 marks available in total — as above]

4 $BC^2 = 11^2 - 7^2 = 72$ so $BC = \sqrt{72} = 6\sqrt{2}$ *[1 mark]*
$BD = \dfrac{6\sqrt{2}}{\cos 30°} = 9.797...$ cm *[1 mark]*
So the radius of the semicircle is $9.797 \div 2 = 4.898...$ cm *[1 mark]*
So the area of the semicircle $= \dfrac{\pi \times (4.898...)^2}{2}$
$= 37.699...$ cm^2
$= 37.7$ cm^2 (1 d.p.) *[1 mark]*
[4 marks available in total — as above]

5 a) Angle $ECA = 90°$ as a tangent meets a radius at 90°.
$AC = 4 \times \tan 58° = 6.401...$ cm *[1 mark]*
So the radius of the circle is $6.401... \div 2 = 3.200...$ cm *[1 mark]*
Area of the circle $= \pi \times 3.200...^2 = 32.183...$
$= 32.18$ cm^2 (2 d.p.) *[1 mark]*
[3 marks available in total — as above]

 b) Angle $ABC = 90°$ and angle $CAB = 180° - 90° - 58° = 32°$
$AB = 6.401... \times \cos 32° = 5.428...$ cm
$BC = 6.401... \times \sin 32° = 3.392...$ cm *[1 mark for both]*
Area of triangle $ABC = 0.5 \times 5.428... \times 3.392...$
$= 9.207...$ cm^2 *[1 mark]*
Angle $ADC = 90°$
$AD = 6.401... \times \cos 53° = 3.852...$ cm
$DC = 6.401... \times \sin 53° = 5.112...$ cm *[1 mark for both]*
Area of triangle $ADC = 0.5 \times 3.852... \times 5.112...$
$= 9.847...$ cm^2 *[1 mark]*
Shaded area $= 32.183... - 9.207... - 9.847...$
$= 13.128... = 13.13$ cm^2 (2 d.p.) *[1 mark]*
[5 marks available in total — as above]
There are other angles you can use to get the side lengths of the triangles but they will all give the same answer.

Pages 56-58: The Sine and Cosine Rules

1 Using Pythagoras:
$AC^2 = 8^2 + 6^2 \Rightarrow AC^2 = 100 \Rightarrow AC = 10$ *[1 mark]*
Using the sine rule: $\sin x = 10 \times \dfrac{\sin 40°}{8}$ *[1 mark]*
$\Rightarrow \sin x = 0.803....$
$\Rightarrow x = \sin^{-1}(0.803...) = 53.46...°$ *[1 mark]*
Angle is obtuse so $x = 180° - 53.46...°$
$= 126.53...° = 127°$ (3 s.f.) *[1 mark]*
[4 marks available in total — as above]

2 Using the sine rule: $\dfrac{BD}{\sin 30°} = \dfrac{5}{\sin 70°}$ *[1 mark]*
$BD = \dfrac{5}{\sin 70°} \times \sin 30° = 2.660...$ m *[1 mark]*
$\dfrac{4}{\sin BDC} = \dfrac{2.660...}{\sin 20°}$ *[1 mark]*
$\sin BDC = \dfrac{\sin 20°}{2.660...} \times 4 = 0.514...$ *[1 mark]*
Angle $BDC = \sin^{-1}(0.514...) = 30.946...°$
So angle $ADC = 70° + 30.946...° = 100.9°$ (1 d.p.) *[1 mark]*
[5 marks available in total — as above]

3 Use the cosine rule to find the missing side of triangle DEF:
$EF^2 = (3\sqrt{2})^2 + 9^2 - (2 \times 3\sqrt{2} \times 9 \times \cos 45°)$ *[1 mark]*
$= 18 + 81 - 54 = 45$ *[1 mark]*
$EF = \sqrt{45} = 3\sqrt{5}$ cm *[1 mark]*
The sides are proportional — all the sides in triangle ABC are $\sqrt{5}$ times longer than the equivalent sides in triangle FDE (e.g. $9 \times \sqrt{5} = 9\sqrt{5}$) so they are similar. *[1 mark]*
[4 marks available in total — as above]

4 Start by working out the radius, r, of the circle:
angle ODC = angle $OCD = (180° - 74°) \div 2 = 53°$
$\dfrac{r}{\sin 53°} = \dfrac{18}{\sin 74°}$, so $r = \dfrac{18}{\sin 74°} \times \sin 53° = 14.954...$ cm
Area $X = \dfrac{26}{360} \times \pi \times 14.954...^2 = 50.743...$ cm^2
Area of triangle $ODC = \dfrac{1}{2} \times 14.954... \times 14.954... \times \sin 74°$
$= 107.490...$ cm^2
Area $Y = \dfrac{74}{360} \times \pi \times 14.954...^2 - 107.490... = 36.932...$ cm^2
So area X is bigger.
[6 marks available — 1 mark for working out angle ODC or OCD, 1 mark for substituting the numbers into the sine rule correctly, 1 mark for the correct radius of the circle, 1 mark for working out area X, 1 mark for working out the area of triangle ODC, 1 mark for working out area Y with a correct answer]

5 Use the cosine rule to find BD and EB
$BD^2 = 15^2 + 12^2 - 2 \times 15 \times 12 \times \cos 77° = 288.017...$
So $BD = 16.971...$ cm
$EB^2 = 14^2 + 11^2 - 2 \times 14 \times 11 \times \cos 73° = 226.949...$
So $EB = 15.064...$ cm
Use the sine rule to find angle DBC and angle ABE:
$\dfrac{16.971...}{\sin 77°} = \dfrac{12}{\sin DBC}$, so $\sin DBC = \dfrac{12 \times \sin 77°}{16.971...} = 0.688...$
So angle $DBC = \sin^{-1}(0.688...) = 43.548...°$
$\dfrac{15.064...}{\sin 73°} = \dfrac{14}{\sin ABE}$, so $\sin ABE = \dfrac{14 \times \sin 73°}{15.064...} = 0.888...$
So angle $ABE = \sin^{-1}(0.888...) = 62.711...°$
Angle $EBD = 129° - 43.548...° - 62.711...° = 22.740...°$
Area $BED = \dfrac{1}{2} \times 16.971... \times 15.064... \times \sin 22.740...°$
$= 49.414... = 49.4$ cm^2 (3 s.f.)
[5 marks available — 1 mark for finding BD, 1 mark for finding EB, 1 mark for finding angle DBC, 1 mark for finding angle ABE, 1 mark for the correct answer]
You could have found angles DBC and ABE using the cosine rule.

6 $AB = x$ cm and $AB:BC = 1:2$, so $BC = 2x$ cm
So $\dfrac{1}{2} \times x \times 2x \times \sin 50° = 38$
$x^2 = \dfrac{38}{\sin 50°} = 49.605...$, so $x = 7.043...$
So $AB = 7.043...$ cm and $BC = 7.043... \times 2 = 14.086...$ cm
Use the cosine rule to find AC:
$AC^2 = 7.043...^2 + 14.086...^2 - 2 \times 7.043... \times 14.086... \times \cos 50°$
$= 120.484...$, so $AC = 10.976... = 11.0$ cm (3 s.f.)
[4 marks available — 1 mark for setting up an equation for the area of the triangle, 1 mark for finding the length of AB, 1 mark for a correct method to find side AC, 1 mark for the correct answer]

7 Angle CAO = angle CBO = 90°
So angle ACB = 360° − 118° − 90° − 90° = 62°
Angle CAB = angle CBA = (180° − 62°) ÷ 2 = 59°
Using the cosine rule to find BA:
$BA^2 = 8.5^2 + 8.5^2 − 2 \times 8.5 \times 8.5 \times \cos 118°$ = 212.338...
So BA = 14.571... cm
Use the sine rule to find CA: $\dfrac{CA}{\sin 59°} = \dfrac{14.571...}{\sin 62°}$

$CA = \sin 59° \times \dfrac{14.571...}{\sin 62°}$ = 14.146... cm
So area of triangle $ABC = \frac{1}{2} \times 14.571... \times 14.146... \times \sin 59°$
$\qquad\qquad = 88.347...$ cm²

Area of triangle $OAB = \frac{1}{2} \times 8.5 \times 8.5 \times \sin 118°$ = 31.896... cm²

So area of minor segment $= \left(\dfrac{118}{360} \times \pi \times 8.5^2\right) − 31.896...$
$\qquad\qquad\qquad\qquad\qquad = 42.502...$ cm²

Subtract the area of the minor segment from the area of
triangle ABC: 88.347... − 42.502... = 45.845... = 45.8 cm² (3 s.f.)
[7 marks available — 1 mark for finding angles ACB and CAB/
CBA, 1 mark for finding the length of BA, 1 mark for finding CA
or CB, 1 mark for finding the area of triangle ABC, 1 mark for
working out the area of triangle OAB, 1 mark for finding the area
of the minor segment, 1 mark for the correct answer]

Pages 59-60: 3D Pythagoras and Trigonometry

1 The vertical height of each cone is 6 m ÷ 2 = 3 m
Let the radius of the cones be r, then, using Pythagoras:
$r^2 = 4.2^2 − 3^2 = 8.64$ so r = 2.939... m *[1 mark]*
Volume of one cone $= \frac{1}{3} \times \pi \times 2.939...^2 \times 3$
$\qquad\qquad\qquad = 27.143...$ m³ *[1 mark]*
Volume of the whole solid = 27.143... × 2
$\qquad\qquad\qquad\qquad\qquad = 54.286... = 54.3$ m³ (3 s.f.) *[1 mark]*
[3 marks available in total — as above]

2 Using Pythagoras' theorem on triangle AXV:
$AX^2 = 8.9^2 − 7.2^2 = 27.37$, so $AX = \sqrt{27.37}$ *[1 mark]*
and $AC = 2\sqrt{27.37}$ *[1 mark]*
Now using Pythagoras' theorem on triangle ABC:
$AB^2 = (2\sqrt{27.37})^2 − 4.2^2 = 91.84$ *[1 mark]*,
so $AB = \sqrt{91.84}$ = 9.583... = 9.58 cm (3 s.f.) *[1 mark]*
[4 marks available in total — as above]

3 XE = 8 cm as the hexagon is made from equilateral triangles.
Let Y be the midpoint of ED, then EXY is a right-angled triangle.
$XY^2 = 8^2 − 4^2 = 48$, so $XY = \sqrt{48}$ cm *[1 mark]*
The angle between planes VED and $ABCDEF$ is angle VYX.

$\tan VYX = \dfrac{15}{\sqrt{48}}$ *[1 mark]*, so $VYX = \tan^{-1}\left(\dfrac{15}{\sqrt{48}}\right)$

VYX = 65.208... = 65.2° (1 d.p.) *[1 mark]*
[3 marks available in total — as above]

4 a) The required angle is angle HBE
$\quad BE^2 = 5^2 + 5^2 = 50$, so $BE = \sqrt{50}$ *[1 mark]*

$\quad \tan HBE = \dfrac{7}{\sqrt{50}}$ *[1 mark]*

$\quad$ So $HBE = \tan^{-1}\left(\dfrac{7}{\sqrt{50}}\right)$ = 44.710...° = 44.7° (3 s.f.) *[1 mark]*

$\quad$ *[3 marks available in total — as above]*
$\quad$ *You could have found length HB instead of BE.*

b) $MN^2 = 7^2 + 5^2 = 74$, so $MN = \sqrt{74}$ *[1 mark]*
$\quad$ Then BMN is a right-angled triangle.

$\quad \tan BMN = \dfrac{2.5}{\sqrt{74}}$ *[1 mark]*

$\quad$ So $BMN = \tan^{-1}\left(\dfrac{2.5}{\sqrt{74}}\right)$ = 16.204...°

$\quad$ So angle BMF = 16.204... × 2 = 32.4° (3 s.f.) *[1 mark]*
$\quad$ *[3 marks available in total — as above]*
$\quad$ *There are other methods you could use here — e.g. you could find*
$\quad$ *MB instead of MN and use that to find the angle.*

5 $AN = 12 \times \dfrac{3}{4}$ = 9 cm and ND = 12 − 9 = 3 cm *[1 mark for both]*
In triangle CNF: CF = 12 cm
$CN^2 = 8^2 + 9^2 + 4^2 = 161$ so $CN = \sqrt{161}$ cm *[1 mark]*
$NF^2 = 3^2 + 8^2 + 4^2 = 89$ so $NF = \sqrt{89}$ cm *[1 mark]*
Now use the cosine rule to find angle CNF:
$\cos CNF = \dfrac{\sqrt{161}^2 + \sqrt{89}^2 − 12^2}{2 \times \sqrt{161} \times \sqrt{89}}$ *[1 mark]* = 0.442...
Angle $CNF = \cos^{-1}(0.442...)$ = 63.719...° = 63.7° (1 d.p.) *[1 mark]*
[5 marks available in total — as above]

Pages 61-62: Vectors

1 $AL:LD$ is 1:3 so $\overrightarrow{DA} = 4\mathbf{a}$ *[1 mark]*
$\overrightarrow{AB} = 2\mathbf{b}$ as M is the midpoint so $\overrightarrow{DC} = 2\mathbf{b}$ and $\overrightarrow{CD} = −2\mathbf{b}$
$\overrightarrow{CA} = \overrightarrow{CD} + \overrightarrow{DA} = −2\mathbf{b} + 4\mathbf{a}$ or $4\mathbf{a} − 2\mathbf{b}$ *[1 mark]*
$\overrightarrow{CA} = 4\begin{pmatrix} −3 \\ −1 \end{pmatrix} − 2\begin{pmatrix} 2 \\ −4 \end{pmatrix} = \begin{pmatrix} −12 \\ −4 \end{pmatrix} − \begin{pmatrix} 4 \\ 8 \end{pmatrix} = \begin{pmatrix} −16 \\ −12 \end{pmatrix}$ *[1 mark]*
Magnitude of $\overrightarrow{CA} = \sqrt{16^2 + 12^2} = \sqrt{400}$ = 20 *[1 mark]*
[4 marks available in total — as above]

2 a) PQD and ACD are similar, and $AD:PD$ = 5:3,
$\quad$ so $\overrightarrow{CA} = \dfrac{5}{3} \times \overrightarrow{QP} = \dfrac{5}{3}\mathbf{b}$ *[1 mark]*

b) $\overrightarrow{PR} = \overrightarrow{PA} + \overrightarrow{AR}$
$\quad AD:PD$ = 5:3 so $AP:PD$ = 2:3 and $3\overrightarrow{PA} = 2\overrightarrow{DP}$
$\quad \overrightarrow{PA} = \dfrac{2}{3}\overrightarrow{DP} = \dfrac{2}{3}(−\mathbf{a} + \mathbf{b}) = −\dfrac{2}{3}\mathbf{a} + \dfrac{2}{3}\mathbf{b}$ *[1 mark]*
$\quad \overrightarrow{AR} = \dfrac{2}{5}\overrightarrow{AC} = −\dfrac{2}{5}\overrightarrow{CA} = −\dfrac{2}{5} \times \dfrac{5}{3}\mathbf{b} = −\dfrac{2}{3}\mathbf{b}$ *[1 mark]*
$\quad \overrightarrow{PR} = −\dfrac{2}{3}\mathbf{a} + \dfrac{2}{3}\mathbf{b} − \dfrac{2}{3}\mathbf{b} = −\dfrac{2}{3}\mathbf{a}$
$\quad \overrightarrow{DQ} = −\mathbf{a}$ so $k = \dfrac{2}{3}$ *[1 mark]*
$\quad$ *[3 marks available in total — as above]*

3 E.g. $\overrightarrow{AC}$ and $\overrightarrow{AE}$ are parallel vectors as ACE is a straight line.
$\overrightarrow{AC} = k\mathbf{b} + 6\mathbf{a}$ *[1 mark]*
$\overrightarrow{AE} = \overrightarrow{AB} + \overrightarrow{BE} = 6\mathbf{a} + (4\mathbf{a} + 25\mathbf{b}) = 10\mathbf{a} + 25\mathbf{b}$ *[1 mark]*
Comparing the coefficients of $\mathbf{a}$, $\overrightarrow{AE} = \dfrac{10}{6}\overrightarrow{AC}$ *[1 mark]*
So $k = 25 \div \dfrac{10}{6}$ = 15 *[1 mark]*
[4 marks available in total — as above]
There are other ways to solve this question — if you got the answer
and showed your working then you'll get full marks.

4 E.g. $AB:BC:CD$ = 4:3:4
$\overrightarrow{AB} = 3\mathbf{a}$, $\overrightarrow{BC} = 3\mathbf{a} \times \dfrac{3}{4} = \dfrac{9}{4}\mathbf{a}$ and $\overrightarrow{CD} = 3\mathbf{a}$ *[1 mark]*
$\overrightarrow{FE} = \overrightarrow{CD} = 3\mathbf{a}$
$\overrightarrow{AE} = \overrightarrow{AF} + \overrightarrow{FE} = (\dfrac{15}{4}\mathbf{a} + 2\mathbf{b}) + 3\mathbf{a} = \dfrac{27}{4}\mathbf{a} + 2\mathbf{b}$ *[1 mark]*
$\overrightarrow{FC} = \overrightarrow{FA} + \overrightarrow{AC} = −(\dfrac{15}{4}\mathbf{a} + 2\mathbf{b}) + 3\mathbf{a} + \dfrac{9}{4}\mathbf{a} = \dfrac{3}{2}\mathbf{a} − 2\mathbf{b}$ *[1 mark]*
$4\overrightarrow{FM} = \overrightarrow{MC}$ so $\overrightarrow{FM} = \dfrac{1}{5}\overrightarrow{FC} = \dfrac{1}{5}(\dfrac{3}{2}\mathbf{a} − 2\mathbf{b}) = \dfrac{3}{10}\mathbf{a} − \dfrac{2}{5}\mathbf{b}$
$\overrightarrow{AM} = \overrightarrow{AF} + \overrightarrow{FM} = (\dfrac{15}{4}\mathbf{a} + 2\mathbf{b}) + (\dfrac{3}{10}\mathbf{a} − \dfrac{2}{5}\mathbf{b})$
$\qquad\qquad = \dfrac{81}{20}\mathbf{a} + \dfrac{8}{5}\mathbf{b}$ *[1 mark]*
$\overrightarrow{AM}$ is not a scalar multiple of $\overrightarrow{AE}$ so they are not parallel
and so AME is not a straight line. *[1 mark]*
[5 marks available in total — as above]
You could have shown that $\overrightarrow{AM}$ and $\overrightarrow{ME}$ aren't parallel instead.

Section Six – Statistics and Probability

Pages 63-64: Comparing Data Sets

1   The median is at the $(27 + 1) \div 2 = $ 14th value.
There are $2 + 1 + 4 + 6 = 13$ ratings of 4 or below
so the 14th value (median) is a rating of 5. *[1 mark]*
Lower quartile is at $(27 + 1) \div 4 = $ 7th value and the upper quartile
is at the $3(27 + 1) \div 4 = $ 21st value.
Lower quartile of website B = 3, Upper quartile of website B = 6
so interquartile range = $6 - 3 = 3$ *[1 mark]*
The median for website A was higher, so on average people rated
website A higher than website B. Therefore they liked website A
more than website B. *[1 mark]*
The interquartile range for A was larger, so the ratings for
website A were more spread out than website B. Therefore people
had more varied opinions of website A than website B. *[1 mark]*
[4 marks available in total — as above]

2   The tickets took 30 minutes to sell out in 2013 but only 24 minutes
in 2014 so they sold out quicker in 2014.
The median in 2013 was 12.5 minutes. So the first half of the
tickets sold out quicker in 2013 then slowed down, whereas in
2014, sales started slowly then sped up.
The interquartile range in 2013 was $15.5 - 10 = 5.5$ minutes and in
2014 it was 3 minutes. Ticket sales were more concentrated around
the median time in 2014 as the interquartile range is smaller.
*[4 marks available — 1 mark for comparing the times it took the
tickets to sell out, 1 mark for finding and comparing the medians,
1 mark for working out the interquartile range in 2013, 1 mark
for comparing the interquartile ranges]*

3   a) (i) E.g. The maximum range of house prices in town A is
£360 000 – £200 000 = £160 000.
The minimum range of house prices in town B is
£340 000 – £180 000 = £160 000.
So the statement is incorrect the range of house prices in
town A cannot be greater than the range for town B.
*[2 marks available — 1 mark for working out the range
of house prices in each town, 1 mark for a correct
comparison]*
(ii) E.g. It is impossible to tell — the histogram doesn't have
a scale on the frequency density axis. You can only tell
the proportion of houses in certain price brackets, not the
number of houses.
*[2 marks available — 1 mark for saying you can't tell this
from the histogram, 1 mark for a correct explanation]*

b) Work out the proportion of houses between £280 000 and
£320 000 in each town by counting the number of squares of
the histogram they take up.
In town A: 8 big squares are between £280 000 and £320 000.
There are 24 squares in the histogram. The proportion of
houses between £280 000 and £320 000 is $\frac{8}{24} = \frac{1}{3}$.
In town B: 10 big squares are between £280 000 and £320 000.
There are 40 squares in the histogram. The proportion of
houses between £280 000 and £320 000 is $\frac{10}{40} = \frac{1}{4}$.
$\frac{1}{3} > \frac{1}{4}$ so there is a higher proportion of houses between
£280 000 and £320 000 in town A.
*[4 marks available in total — 1 mark for the correct method
to work out the proportions, 1 mark for the correct proportion
for town A, 1 mark for the correct proportion for town B,
1 mark for the correct answer]*

Pages 65-66: Histograms

1    $70 < t \le 85$ has a frequency of 39. Class width $= 85 - 70 = 15$.
The frequency density for the class $70 < t \le 85$ is $39 \div 15 = 2.6$, so

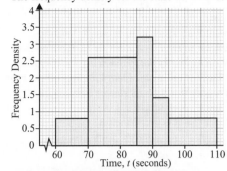

Time t (seconds)	Frequency
$60 < t \le 70$	$10 \times 0.8 = 8$
$70 < t \le 85$	$15 \times 2.6 = 39$
$85 < t \le 90$	$5 \times 3.2 = 16$
$90 < t \le 95$	$5 \times 1.4 = 7$
$95 < t \le 110$	$15 \times 0.8 = 12$

Total number of members $= 8 + 39 + 16 + 7 + 12 = 82$
*[4 marks available in total — 1 mark for finding the frequency
density of the $70 < t \le 85$ class, 1 mark for using this to find the
frequency densities of the other classes, 1 mark for finding the
frequencies of each class, 1 mark for the correct answer]*

2   a) Start by working out the frequency of bouncy balls in each class:
The whole histogram represents 600 bouncy balls and there are
30 big squares in the histogram so each big square represents
$600 \div 30 = 20$ bouncy balls.

Weight w (grams)	Frequency
$40 < w \le 41$	$20 \times 4 = 80$
$41 < w \le 41.5$	$20 \times 4 = 80$
$41.5 < w \le 42.5$	$20 \times 6 = 120$
$42.5 < w \le 43.5$	$20 \times 12 = 240$
$43.5 < w \le 44$	$20 \times 4 = 80$

To estimate the mean, first multiply the mid-point of each class
by the frequency: $(40.5 \times 80) + (41.25 \times 80) + (42 \times 120)$
$+ (43 \times 240) + (43.75 \times 80) = 25\,400$
So mean $= 25\,400 \div 600 = 42.3333... = 42.3$ g (to 1 d.p.)
*[5 marks available — 1 mark for a correct method to work out
the frequency of each class, 1 mark for the correct frequencies
for each class, 1 mark for multiplying the mid-points of each
class by the frequencies, 1 mark for dividing by 600 to find the
mean, 1 mark for the correct answer]*

b) E.g. The median weight is between the 300th and 301st ball,
which are both in the class $42.5 < w \le 43.5$ so Sumi is correct.
*[2 marks available — 1 mark for saying she is correct,
1 mark for a correct explanation]*

3   a) The frequencies are given by the area of each bar.

Height (metres)	Frequency
1 to 2	$1 \times 12 = 12$
2 to 2.5	$0.5 \times 32 = 16$
2.5 to 2.75	$0.25 \times 88 = 22$
2.75 to 3	$0.25 \times 72 = 18$
3 to 4	$1 \times 12 = 12$

[1 mark]

Total $= 12 + 16 + 22 + 18 + 12 = 80$
Estimate of number of statues between 1.75 m to 2.75 m
$= ((2 - 1.75) \times 12) + 16 + 22 = 41$ *[1 mark]*
Percentage $= (41 \div 80) \times 100 = 51.25\%$ *[1 mark]*
[3 marks available in total — as above]

b) To estimate the mean height, first multiply the midpoint of each interval by the frequency: $(1.5 \times 12) + (2.25 \times 16) + (2.625 \times 22) + (2.875 \times 18) + (3.5 \times 12)$
$= 18 + 36 + 57.75 + 51.75 + 42 = 205.5$
Estimate of mean = $205.5 \div 80$
$= 2.57$ metres (2 d.p.) which is more than 2.5 metres.
[3 marks available in total — 1 mark for multiplying the mid-points of each class by the frequencies, 1 mark for dividing by 80 to find the mean, 1 mark for the correct answer]

c) There are $16 + 22 + 18 + 12 = 68$ statues over 2 metres.
There are 12 statues over 3 metres.
P(over 3 metres given it is over 2 metres) $= \frac{12}{68} = \frac{3}{17}$.
[2 marks available — 1 mark for correct calculation, 1 mark for the correct answer]

Pages 67-68: Probability

1 a) Frequency of odd number $= 54 + 38 + 61 = 153$
Relative frequency of an odd number $= \frac{153}{200} = 0.765$
[2 marks available — 1 mark for a correct method, 1 mark for the correct answer]

b) E.g. the relative frequency of getting a 5 is $\frac{61}{200} = 0.305$ which is less than 0.5, so he is actually unlikely to get a 5.
[1 mark for any valid explanation]

2 a) Let $x = $ P(3). Then P(1) = $3x$, so P(odd) $= x + 3x = 4x$
P(even) $= 2 \times$ P(odd) $= 2 \times 4x = 8x$
P(even) + P(odd) $= 1$, so $4x + 8x = 12x = 1$
$x = \frac{1}{12}$, so P(3) $= \frac{1}{12}$
[2 marks available — 1 mark for finding expressions for the probabilities, 1 mark for the correct answer]

b) P(1 even and 1 odd) = P(even, odd) + P(odd, even)
$= \left(\frac{2}{3} \times \frac{1}{3}\right) + \left(\frac{1}{3} \times \frac{2}{3}\right) = \frac{4}{9}$
[2 marks available — 1 mark for a correct method, 1 mark for the correct answer]

c) P(even, even, even) $= \frac{2}{3} \times \frac{2}{3} \times \frac{2}{3} = \frac{8}{27}$ *[1 mark]*
P(odd) $= \frac{1}{3} = \frac{9}{27}$ so she is more likely to spin an odd number first time. *[1 mark]*
[2 marks available in total — as above]

3 $G_A G_B = 0.24$ [1]
$G_A B_B = 0.56$ and $B_B = 1 - G_B$
So, $G_A(1 - G_B) = 0.56$, which means $G_A - G_A G_B = 0.56$ [2]
Substitute [1] into [2]: $G_A - 0.24 = 0.56$, so $G_A = 0.8$
Putting this value back into [1]: $0.8G_B = 0.24$, so $G_B = 0.3$
So in Year 9 there are $(30 \times 0.8) + (30 \times 0.3) = 33$ girls
[4 marks available — 1 mark for forming the two simultaneous equations, 1 mark for finding G_A, 1 mark for finding G_B, 1 mark for the correct answer]

4 At the start, Bag A: P(red) $= \frac{n}{n + 14}$ and Bag B: P(red) $= \frac{30}{30 + n}$
When 2 blue balls are moved,
Bag A contains 12 blue and n red so P(red) $= \frac{n}{n + 12}$ *[1 mark]*
Bag B contains 30 red and $n + 2$ blue, so P(red) $= \frac{30}{n + 32}$ *[1 mark]*
The probabilities are equal so: $\frac{n}{n + 12} = \frac{30}{n + 32}$
$n(n + 32) = 30(n + 12)$ *[1 mark]*
$n^2 + 32n = 30n + 360$
$n^2 + 2n - 360 = 0$ *[1 mark]*
$(n - 18)(n + 20) = 0$, so $n = 18$ (as n must be positive) *[1 mark]*
The original probability of picking a red ball from Bag B is
$\frac{30}{30 + 18} = \frac{30}{48} = \frac{5}{8}$ *[1 mark]*
[6 marks available in total — as above]

Pages 69-71: Tree Diagrams

1 a)
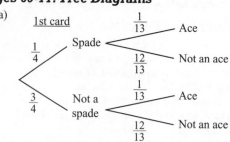

[2 marks available in total — 2 marks for a fully correct tree diagram, otherwise 1 mark for at least 3 correct probabilities]

b) P(not a spade and not an ace) $= \frac{3}{4} \times \frac{12}{13} = \frac{36}{52} = \frac{9}{13}$ *[1 mark]*

For questions 2-4, you can draw tree diagrams to help you if you want.

2 a) There are 5 prime numbers between 1 and 12 so P(prime) $= \frac{5}{12}$
P(3 prime numbers) = P(prime) $\times$ P(prime) $\times$ P(prime)
$= \frac{5}{12} \times \frac{5}{12} \times \frac{5}{12} = \frac{125}{1728}$
[2 marks available — 1 mark for the correct probability of a prime number, 1 mark for the correct answer]

b) P(roll < 5) $= \frac{1}{3}$ and P(roll $\geq$ 5) $= \frac{2}{3}$
P(one roll < 5) = P(1st number is < 5, other 2 are $\geq$ 5)
        + P(2nd number is < 5, other 2 are $\geq$ 5)
        + P(3rd number is < 5, other 2 are $\geq$ 5)
P (one roll < 5) $= \left(\frac{1}{3} \times \frac{2}{3} \times \frac{2}{3}\right) + \left(\frac{2}{3} \times \frac{1}{3} \times \frac{2}{3}\right) + \left(\frac{2}{3} \times \frac{2}{3} \times \frac{1}{3}\right)$
$= \frac{12}{27} = \frac{4}{9}$
[3 marks available — 1 mark for the correct probabilities for less than a 5 and 5 or more, 1 mark for a correct method for finding the answer, 1 mark for the correct answer]

3 P(less than 5 fish) = 1 − P(5 or more fish)
P(5 or more fish) = P(1, 2, 2) + P(2, 1, 2) + P(2, 2, 1) + P(2, 2, 2)
$= (0.5 \times 0.3 \times 0.3) + (0.3 \times 0.5 \times 0.3) + (0.3 \times 0.3 \times 0.5)$
        $+ (0.3 \times 0.3 \times 0.3) = 0.045 + 0.045 + 0.045 + 0.027 = 0.162$
P(less than 5 fish) = 1 − 0.162 = 0.838
[4 marks available in total — 1 mark for finding the outcomes that will give 5 or more fish, 1 mark for calculating the probability of each of the outcomes, 1 mark for adding the probabilities together, 1 mark for the correct answer]

4 a) There are $6 \times 6 = 36$ possible outcomes and there are three ways to win the game (rolling a 5 and 6, 6 and 5, or 6 and 6).
So the probability of winning is $\frac{3}{36} = \frac{1}{12}$.
So you'd estimate that a prize will be won every 12 games.
If there are 20 prizes, you'd estimate that the stall will run out of prizes after $12 \times 20 = 240$ games.
It takes £2 each go, so expected takings are $240 \times £2 = £480$.
[3 marks available — 1 mark for finding the number of winning outcomes, 1 mark for the correct probability of winning, 1 mark for explaining why this means you'd estimate 240 games will be played and therefore £480 will be taken]

b) P(wins at least one prize) = 1 − P(no prizes)
P(no prizes) $= \frac{11}{12} \times \frac{11}{12} = \frac{121}{144}$ *[1 mark]*
P(wins at least one prize) $= 1 - \frac{121}{144}$ *[1 mark]* $= \frac{23}{144}$ *[1 mark]*
[3 marks available in total — as above]

5

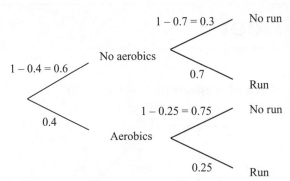

P(no run)
= P(no aerobics and no run) + P(aerobics and no run)
P(no aerobics and no run) = 0.6 × 0.3 = 0.18
P(aerobics and no run) = 0.4 × 0.75 = 0.3
So P(no run) = 0.18 + 0.3 = 0.48
[3 marks available — 1 mark for finding the missing probabilities,
1 mark for a correct method, 1 mark for the correct answer]
You could also find the probability that he goes for a run
(0.6 × 0.7) + (0.4 × 0.25) = 0.52 and subtract it from 1.

For questions 6-7, you can draw tree diagrams to help you if you want.

6   a)   P(at least one prize) = 1 – P(no prizes)
20 tickets end in a 0 or 5 so the probability of picking a
winning ticket is $\frac{20}{100}$ and a losing ticket is $\frac{80}{100}$. *[1 mark]*

P(no prizes) = $\frac{80}{100} \times \frac{79}{99} = \frac{316}{495}$ *[1 mark]*

P(at least one prize) = 1 – $\frac{316}{495}$ *[1 mark]* = $\frac{179}{495}$ *[1 mark]*

[4 marks available in total — as above]

   b)   There are 100 – 40 = 60 tickets left and 20 – 5 = 15 of them
are winning tickets so the probability of picking a winning

ticket is $\frac{15}{60}$ and a losing ticket is $\frac{45}{60}$.

P(no prizes) = $\frac{45}{60} \times \frac{44}{59} = \frac{33}{59}$

P(at least one prize) = 1 – $\frac{33}{59} = \frac{26}{59} = 0.440...$

$\frac{179}{495} = 0.361...$

0.440... > 0.361... so her chances of winning
are better than Amy's.
[3 marks available in total — 1 mark for working out the
probability of picking a losing ticket, 1 mark for calculating
the probability of Carla winning at least one prize, 1 mark
for saying she has a better chance to win by comparing the
fractions]

7   P(picking a green counter) = $\frac{n}{n+(n+1)} = \frac{n}{2n+1}$ *[1 mark]*

P(picking a blue counter) = $\frac{n+1}{n+(n+1)} = \frac{n+1}{2n+1}$ *[1 mark]*

P(picking 2 green counters) = $\frac{n}{2n+1} \times \frac{n-1}{2n} = \frac{n-1}{4n+2}$ *[1 mark]*

P(picking 2 blue counters) = $\frac{n+1}{2n+1} \times \frac{n}{2n} = \frac{n+1}{4n+2}$ *[1 mark]*

P(both counters are the same) = $\frac{n-1}{4n+2} + \frac{n+1}{4n+2}$

$= \frac{2n}{4n+2} = \frac{n}{2n+1}$ *[1 mark]*

[5 marks available in total — as above]

Pages 72-73: Probability from Venn Diagrams

1   a) $2n + 1$ generates set A = {3, 5, 7, 9, 11, 13, 15, 17, 19}
$\frac{n(n+1)}{2}$ generates set B = {1, 3, 6, 10, 15}

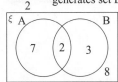

[3 marks available — 3 marks for a completely correct Venn
diagram, otherwise 1 mark for listing or finding the number
of elements in set A and 1 mark for listing or finding the
number of elements in set B]

   b) $\frac{2}{20} = \frac{1}{10}$ *[1 mark]*

2   a)   106 + 19 = 125 students attend the disco
106 + 19 + 33 + 42 = 200 students in total.
125 : 200 *[1 mark]* = 5 : 8 *[1 mark]*
[2 marks available in total — as above]

   b)   (i) $\frac{19}{125}$

[2 marks available — 1 mark for the correct numerator,
1 mark for the correct denominator]

      (ii) $\frac{106}{139}$

[2 marks available — 1 mark for the correct numerator,
1 mark for the correct denominator]

3   a)

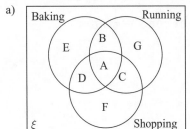

A: 10% of 80 = 0.1 × 80 = 8 *[1 mark]*
B: 22 – 8 = 14   C: 18 – 8 = 10 *[1 mark for both]*
Half the people only liked 1 activity so the other half liked
2 or 3 activities: 0.5 × 80 = 40.
D: 40 – (14 + 10 + 8) = 8 *[1 mark]*
E: 43 – (14 + 8 + 8) = 13
F: 35 – (8 + 8 + 10) = 9 *[1 mark for both E and F]*
G: 80 – (8 + 14 + 10 + 8 + 13 + 9) = 18 *[1 mark]*
[5 marks available in total — as above]

   b) $\frac{14+8+8}{14+8+8+10} = \frac{30}{40} = \frac{3}{4}$

[2 marks available — 1 mark for correct calculation,
1 mark for the correct answer]

4   There are 50 people in the choir, so
$n(n + 2) + n + (2n - 3) + (8 - n) = 50$ *[1 mark]*
$n^2 + 4n + 5 = 50$, so $n^2 + 4n - 45 = 0$
$(n + 9)(n - 5) = 0$, so $n = 5$ (as n has to be positive) *[1 mark]*
The number of people who play the piano is
$n(n + 2) + n = (5 \times 7) + 5 = 40$ *[1 mark]*
P(both play piano) = $\frac{40}{50} \times \frac{39}{49}$ *[1 mark]* = $\frac{156}{245}$ *[1 mark]*
[5 marks available in total — as above]

Formula Sheet

Arithmetic series

Sum to n terms, $S_n = \frac{n}{2}[2a + (n-1)d]$

Area of trapezium $= \frac{1}{2}(a+b)h$

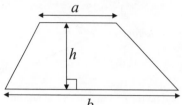

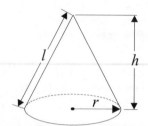

Curved surface area of cone $= \pi r l$

Volume of cone $= \frac{1}{3}\pi r^2 h$

Volume of prism = area of cross section × length

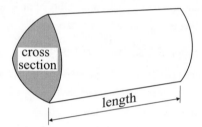

The quadratic equation

The solutions of $ax^2 + bx + c = 0$,
where $a \neq 0$, are given by:

$$x = \frac{-b \pm \sqrt{b^2 - 4ac}}{2a}$$

Volume of sphere $= \frac{4}{3}\pi r^3$

Surface area of sphere $= 4\pi r^2$

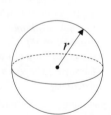

For any triangle ABC:

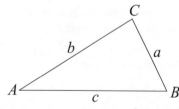

Sine rule: $\dfrac{a}{\sin A} = \dfrac{b}{\sin B} = \dfrac{c}{\sin C}$

Cosine rule: $a^2 = b^2 + c^2 - 2bc\cos A$

Area of triangle $= \frac{1}{2}ab\sin C$

Volume of cylinder $= \pi r^2 h$

Curved surface area of cylinder $= 2\pi r h$

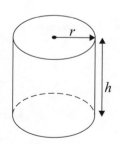